NUMERICAL CONTROL

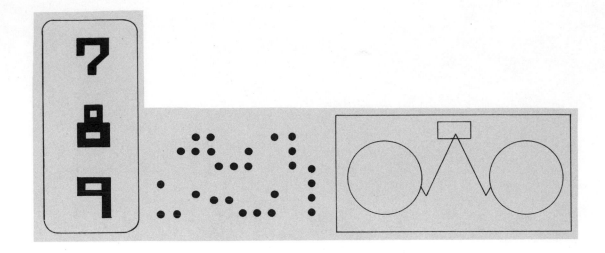

NUMERICAL

Prentice-Hall, Inc.

CONTROL

R. M. Dyke

Senior Member, American Society of
Tool and Manufacturing Engineers;
Member, American Society for Metals,
Society of Carbide Engineers, Numer-
ical Control Society

Englewood Cliffs, New Jersey

NUMERICAL CONTROL

—R. M. Dyke

© 1967, by
PRENTICE-HALL, INC.
Englewood Cliffs, N.J.

Library of Congress
Catalog Card Number: 67–19949

PRINTED IN THE UNITED STATES OF AMERICA
B & P

THE PURPOSE OF NUMERICAL CONTROL

This book is intended primarily for prospective users of numerical control and for those who wish to gain an introductory knowledge of the subject in its many facets. The author hopes, however, that its contents will also assist those who are already making use of numerically controlled equipment in manufacturing and allied activity, and that it will be of value generally to students of machine tool control systems and metalworking manufacturing practice.

Although the numerical control concept is by now well established as having a valuable and important role to play in manufacturing, there are still various misconceptions concerning its purpose and application. Perhaps this can be expected, because the general application of numerical control is relatively new and has not yet been widely documented in book form, even though it was proposed and developed, for the aircraft industry, as far back as 1949.* The early systems, intended chiefly for complex contouring or continuous-path operations, have since then been joined and outnumbered by the simpler point-to-point or positioning controls. With these and other points in mind, if this book helps to clear up some of the misconceptions about numerical control, as the concept is now applied, it will have served part of its purpose.

Numerical control provides a more scientific approach to manufacturing, giving more scope to management in advance planning and in its control over actual manufacturing operations. To achieve the large increases in productivity and in annual economic growth rates which are projected for the years and decades ahead, it is possible that only numerical control—or a similarly based concept, even if bearing a different name—adopted on a greatly increased scale, will prove to be the solution, or be a major factor in it. The rapid growth in the number of numerically controlled installations would indicate that this approach to that solution is well under way; in fact, various important models of machine tools are now available only with numerical control instead of optionally with the conventional type as well. And it may be well to point out at this stage, and as described in the text, that numerical control is not restricted to tape input, as the manual digital input type of numerical control, or "dial input," may also be utilized with tape or separately. Necessarily, the manual-input approach provides a lesser degree of automation and management control.

Changes can be expected in numerical control systems and the machines and apparatus designed to exploit them as an inherent part of progress, but they are bound to be technological rather than fundamental in nature, utilizing more computerization, yet retaining the broad concept of this approach to automation—with its flexibility for short and medium production runs, and even long runs in various cases.

This book would not have been possible without the assistance and cooperation of many machine tool builders and other makers of production and related equipment, systems manufacturers, users of numerical control, societies and associations, and other organizations. In particular, the author wishes to thank the following:

Allen-Bradley Company; American Machine Tool Distributors Association; American SIP Corporation; American Tool Works Company; Avey Machine Tool Company; The Bendix Corporation, Industrial Controls Division; The Boeing Company, Airplane Division—Wichita Branch; Brown & Sharpe Manufacturing Co.; The Bullard Company; The Bunker-Ramo Corporation, Numerical Control

---

* *This was at the Servomechanisms Laboratory, Massachusetts Institute of Technology, following the award of a development contract by the Air Materiel Command, United States Air Force, which in turn was the result of a prior proposal to the USAF by John T. Parsons, of the Parsons Corporation, Aircraft Division. Subsequent to the work at MIT, machine tool builders and systems manufacturers continued the development of numerical control systems.*

Systems; The Cincinnati Milling Machine Co.; Cleereman Machine Tool Corporation; DeVlieg Machine Company; Edlund Division, Monarch Machine Tool Company; Farrand Controls, Inc.; Ferranti Ltd.; The Fosdick Machine Tool Company; Friden, Inc.; General Electric Company, Specialty Control Department; Giddings & Lewis Machine Tool Company; Gisholt Machine Company; George Gorton Machine Company; The G. A. Gray Company; Hillyer Corporation; Hughes Aircraft Company, Industrial Systems Division; International Business Machines Corporation; International Harvester Company; Jones & Lamson, Division of Waterbury Farrel; Kearney & Trecker Corporation; The R. K. LeBlond Machine Tool Company; and Le Maire Machine Tool Company. Further:

The Lodge & Shipley Company; Lucas Machine Division, The New Britain Machine Co.; Machinery and Allied Products Institute; Mimik Tracers Inc.; Monarch Machine Tool Company; Moog Servocontrols, Inc., Hydra-Point Division; Pines Engineering Co., Inc.; Pratt & Whitney Company, Incorporated; Production Engineering Research Association; Seneca Falls Machine Co.; The Sheffield Corporation; Sperry Gyroscope Company of Canada, Ltd.; Square D Company, Industrial Control Division; Sundstrand Machine Tool, Division of Sundstrand Corporation; U. S. Department of Commerce—Metalworking Equipment Division, Business & Defense Services Administration; Unimation Inc.; U. S. Industries, Inc., Automation Division; Wales Strippit Company; Wang Laboratories, Inc.; The Warner & Swasey Co.; Westinghouse Electric Corporation; Wiedemann Division, The Warner & Swasey Co. and Woodward Governor Company.

Thanks are also expressed to member firms of the National Machine Tool Builders' Association not already included among the above, numerous users of numerical control, and other companies and organizations whom it has not been possible to list here. Their assistance is nevertheless greatly appreciated.

—R. M. Dyke

CONTENTS

vii

NUMERICAL CONTROL

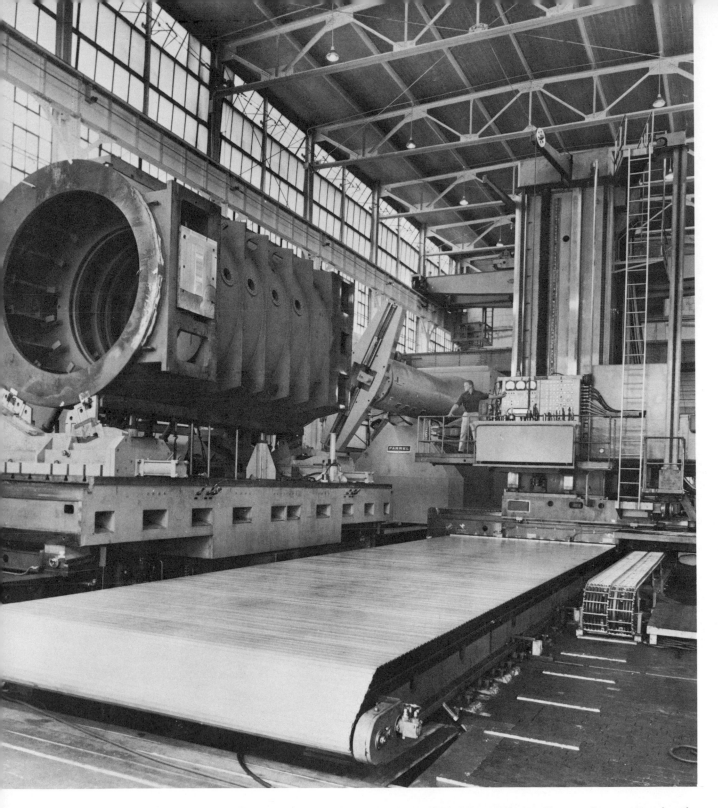

Giant numerically controlled machining center built for Westinghouse Electric Corporation for the production of turbine-generator frames weighing up to 160 tons. Costing $2 million, this machine tool was built by the Rochester division of Farrel Corporation, and the eight-axis numerical control system is by Westinghouse.

The machining center is about 33 ft. high, 53 ft. wide and 100 ft. long, and together with its auxiliary equipment, weighs more than 860 tons.

Most NC equipment, however, is very much smaller and costs only a fraction of the investment represented by this huge machining center.—Courtesy, Westinghouse Electric Corporation.

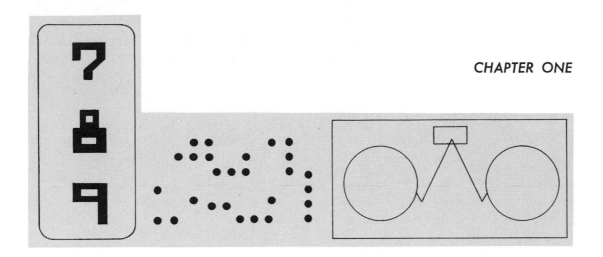

CHAPTER ONE

NUMERICAL CONTROL— FLEXIBLE AUTOMATION

NUMERICAL CONTROL OF MACHINE TOOLS—AND OF OTHER PRODUCTION EQUIPMENT AND PROCESSING—IS AUTOMATION IN ITS MOST FLEXIBLE FORM, WITH ADVANTAGES THAT APPEAL BOTH TO MANAGEMENT AND ENGINEERING. SINCE THE INSTRUCTIONS FOR MACHINE OPERATION ARE PLACED ON THE CONTROL TAPE OR CARDS, THE PLANNING AND DECISIONS FOR DETAILED MACHINE OPERATIONS ARE TAKEN AWAY FROM THE PRODUCTION FLOOR OF THE PLANT AND PLACED UNDER THE DIRECT CONTROL OF MANAGEMENT.

THE PRODUCTION ENGINEERING OFFICE, OR ITS EQUIVALENT, PROGRAMS THE ENTIRE OPERATION: IT PLANS THE SEQUENCE OF ALL INDIVIDUAL OPERATIONS, PREDETERMINES THEM, AND PLACES ALL THE INSTRUCTIONS ON THE TAPE IN PUNCHING OR PREPARING IT; AND, THE MACHINE OBEYS THESE INSTRUCTIONS.

THE OPERATING PRINCIPLE OF NUMERICAL

1

control systems may be defined as the automatic control of machines or operations "by numbers"—numerical data—punched into tape or cards in coded form, or recorded on magnetic tape. The numbers may represent units of distance, time, or other basic data required for the operation of a machine or process, and they may also be fed into a system manually by the use of dials or pushbuttons.

The most common field of application for numerical control is in machine tools and other production equipment—the machines used by many manufacturing industries to turn out a great variety of metal and allied products, from consumer goods to heavy machinery.

Spreading out from metal cutting operations and metal forming, the numerical control concept is increasingly taking over additional functions of the complete manufacturing process, such as inspection and testing.

Numerically controlled machine tools are built in a wide variety of types and sizes. They range from the relatively low-priced, multi-purpose drilling machines to large machining centers capable of performing a wide variety of operations with automatic tool changers. These large machines may cost a third of a million dollars, or even more in special cases. A smaller machining center, one of more usual size, is shown in Figure 1–1. A Kearney & Trecker Corporation machine, it is built with an automatic tool changer which transfers selected tools from the 15-tool rotary magazine to the machine spindle, under tape command. The numerical control console is also shown, with its tape reels in the tape reader, which "reads" the coded numerical instructions or data punched in the tape and transmits the information to the control system.

Production with numerically controlled machine tools is extremely flexible. To change from one type of part to another, it is only necessary to change the tape and perform a minimum of setup operations. Changes in a punched-tape program are readily made by repunching the tape, compared with the costly changes required when using the conventional way with special production tooling. In order to repeat a production run, the tape is simply recalled from storage and installed on the machine.

Another important advantage is that, for machining operations, no great amount of special tooling such as jigs and fixtures (for guiding cutting tools or for holding and aligning workpieces) need be stored. Simple work holding fixtures or clamping methods are usually sufficient.

A special feature of numerical control is that small lots, such as 10–25 parts only per run, and sometimes even single pieces, such as complex templates or special prototype parts, can be produced at lower cost.

Outstanding Advantages

In addition to giving management high manufacturing flexibility and control, numerical control provides many other advantages. One of these, reduction in lead time—the time required to get into production on a new part or product—may be the most important, depending on the individual company's requirements. Shorter lead time helps to speed a product to the market, and improves a company's competitive position. The latter also holds true for contract work and job lot production where numerical control permits better scheduling, on-time delivery and contract fulfillment.

Among the other advantages are these:

1. *Substantial reduction in tooling costs, which may range from 60% to 90%.*
2. *Large reductions in machine setup times, from 65% to 75% and even higher.*

Figures 1–1 & 1–2. At top: A numerically controlled machining center with automatic tool changer. Control console at right, with tape reels in tape reader at upper right of console. (Kearney & Trecker Corporation.) At bottom: Point-to-point or positioning numerical control on a jig borer used for the precision machining of 900 mold cavities. (The Fosdick Machine Tool Company.)

3. *Greatly increased machine utilization times—which may run as high as 90%, against 40% to 50% for manual or conventional operation, depending also on machine type and application.*
4. *Greater uniformity of product.*
5. *More efficient and economical assembly as a result of product uniformity.*
6. *Reduced inspection costs.*

Contrary to some misconceptions, "mass production" quantities are not required for economical NC manufacturing, and computer programming is not indispensable.

How Much Automation to Plan

It is important to recognize and keep in mind that automation *per se* is a matter of *degree*—the extent to which it is practicable and profitable to automate. The same holds true for numerical control.

How much of an operation or of a series of operations to automate—to operate and control automatically and in a programmed, predetermined sequence—depends on the individual plant's requirements and applications. The machine operator usually remains in attendance, even with "full" numerical control, although his duties are then different; he performs other functions or may keep several NC machines supplied and in operation.

Numerical control has the additional quality of flexibility in that it can be selected or introduced in stages, as will be shown. At the same time, it must be stated that numerical control is not a solution to every manufacturing problem. The necessity and cost of its installation must be justified, and in many cases this is possible.

WHAT AUTOMATION CALLS FOR

Automation in itself can be defined in numerous ways, depending on individual viewpoints. Basically, automation calls for performing and controlling automatically as much of an operation or series of operations as is practicable.

There may or may not be feedback in the control system—elements that feed back information from the machine to the control center of an automatic control system and thus provide for any necessary corrective action. (A common example of a feedback unit is a room-temperature thermostat as used with an automatic heating system.)

Before the advent of numerical control, the automatic operation of machine tools, generally speaking, did not include true feedback. However, automatic operation was referred to as automation, and it still is (for example, automotive production on transfer lines, where parts such as engine blocks are automatically transferred from one machining station or machine to the next).

Types of Inputs Used

TAPE INPUT

Numerical control, as noted, makes use of instructions in numerical form punched into tape or cards, or recorded on magnetic tape. Punched tape has for some years proved itself as the most common form of information input for NC systems. The information is usually a representation of dimensions or distances which are expressed numerically.

The command signals sent to the machine by a numerical tape control system may be in the form of pulses, each of which may result in a movement of as small as 0.0001 in., depending on the system's design or selection.

DIAL OR PUSHBUTTON INPUT

"Dial input" is another form of numerical control, as will be described later. The numerical instructions are manually dialed into the system by dials or fed in with pushbuttons, and no tape is used.

This input system is generally used on an optional basis with point-to-point or positioning control. This is the more common one of two main types of numerical control, and it involves machine slide movement from one predetermined point to the next point; the machine table with its workpiece remains stationary when a specified point has been reached at which an operation such as drilling is to take place.

The other main type of numerical control is continuous-path or contouring control. This type is used to machine or produce contours or irregular shapes, and the path of the tool or machine slides is under continuous control.

INPUT THROUGH INITIAL MANUAL OPERATION OF MACHINE

There is another type of allied machine control in which the input into the system is not programmed on tape. The machine, such as a robot for manipulating or transferring parts, is first put through its paces manually by the operator. All of the movements—their direction, extent, timing, and the like—are automatically registered on magnetic tape, a magnetic memory drum or similar device. The machine is then switched over to automatic cycle. The control system, drawing upon the information or "instructions" stored in the memory unit, repeats the motions in the same manner, and keeps doing this for as many cycles as may be required.

DIAL INPUT FOR MAKING CONTROL TAPE

In still another type of control system, or as an optional feature with some punched-tape control systems, a control tape is automatically punched while the first part is being run off under "manual" control with dial input.

The Two Main Types of NC Systems

There are two main types of numerical control as to general function, as mentioned briefly before: point-to-point control, also known as positioning control, and continuous-path control, also called contouring control.

POINT-TO-POINT OR POSITIONING CONTROL

In point-to-point control, as for example on a vertical drilling machine, the machine table which carries the work is moved from one point to the next so as to position the work accurately for the various machining operations that are to be performed at those points.

The table and the workpiece on it remain stationary while the work, such as drilling, boring, reaming, tapping or other operation, is being carried out. In some cases, it may be the cutting tool instead of the table that is moved from one position to the next, but the principle is the same.

The remaining functions of the operator; such as changing tools, speeds and feeds, may also be taken over by the numerical control system, depending on the degree of automation required or justified.

Positioning control replaces drilling jigs in production drilling, and takes the place of other special tooling in other operations requiring exact positioning or locating. It also automates the precision locating function of jig borers, as in Figure 1–2. This shows a point-to-point application on a production jig borer built by The Fosdick Machine Tool Company. Here 900 cavities are sunk in a rubber bottlestopper mold. They must mate exactly with the 900 cavities in the other half of the mold. Nine separate operations per cavity are required, or 8,100 in all. Numerical control cuts the machining time from the 396 hours required by manual operation to 102 hours. Preparing the tape takes an added 4 hours.

Positioning systems with added feed-rate control, or straight-cut control, are used for such operations as the turning of step shafts on lathes and for straight-line cuts in milling operations. In lathe work of this type, the positioning system controls the starting and ending points of the cuts, also the tool slide positions for obtaining the various diameters. Feed-rate control can be an extra or optional feature with a vertical drilling machine, for example, to permit straight-line milling cuts to be taken (as opposed to contouring cuts with a contouring system).

CONTINUOUS-PATH OR CONTOURING CONTROL

With a continuous-path numerical control system, the path of the cutter is controlled to produce a desired outline or form. In most machine tool applications of continuous-path control, however, as in two-dimensional contour milling operations, instead of controlling the cutter path, the system controls the path or motions of the machine table past the rotating but otherwise stationary cutter. The effect is the same.

With this type of system, the controlling action is continuous during the cutting operation or during the movements that are under numerical control. Complex parts may be contour machined or formed in several planes at once with this method. Three-dimensional die sinking or milling is one example. This would call for a three-axis numerical control system (indicating that three axes or three major machine motions [or slides] are numerically controlled).

A close-up of a continuous-path milling operation is shown in Figure 1–3, on a vertical die sinking and profile milling machine as built by the Cincinnati Milling Machine Co. The machine employs punched tape in three-dimensional contour milling of a complex part. Interior profiling of a pocket is also involved in this application.

There are additional types of numerical control systems, combinations or variations of these two main types, which will be described later.

With any type of numerical control, the control system and machine elements accept the coded information or instructions punched into the tape or cards, or as placed on magnetic tape, and translate them into the desired machine movements or actions, as programmed.

Programming or Planning an NC Operation

Programming, in its broadest sense, includes the planning of all the steps necessary to machine or manufacture a part. In its narrower sense, programming is used to denote the planning of an operation sequence and the tape preparation only.

Still another meaning of "programming" in general refers to the setting up and adjusting of a machine control system, including numerical control, to provide a predetermined sequence of machine motions. Any such system may be referred to as "program control," and the term is often used quite loosely. Numerical control, especially by tape, is a form of program control, although the expression is more frequently applied to switching systems

Figure 1–3. Closeup view of a continuous-path or contour milling operation on a complex part. (The Cincinnati Milling Machine Co.)

for presetting machine cycles (these will be described in the chapter on alternatives to numerical control).

The programming operation for numerical control starts with the print of the part, or with the original working drawing. If computer programming is to be used, it speeds up this phase but is not indispensable for the majority of numerical control work. The part may be defined in mathematical terms, or the required operations described in a given computer language.

For complete programming, together with NC processing, it is necessary to include the following basic steps:

1. *Prepare a numerical control drawing of the part. This usually gives all the dimensions as coordinates from a basic reference point or origin.*
2. *Plan the machining or production operations and their sequence, the types of cutting tools and holding devices or fixtures to be used, and the operational data for the machine. Also prepare a tooling or setup sheet for guidance of the shop, as may be required.*
3. *Design and make simple holding fixtures and any other tooling that may be required.*
4. *Prepare or type the program manuscript, or program sheets, which are basically operation-sequence instruction sheets, listing all the required commands (numerical positioning data, functional commands, and the like) in properly coded and standardized form.*
5. *Prepare the tape: punch the tape or cards, or record the operation program on magnetic tape, if this system is used, following the instuctions on the program sheets. Check or verify the tape.*
6. *Install the tape in the tape reader of the machine's NC system.*
7. *Set up the machine itself—the holding fixture, workpiece, and cutting tools, as required. Set cutting tool or work in starting position to coincide with basic reference point on numerical drawing.*
8. *Process or machine the part under numerical control.*

Many of these steps are also required for conventional production, and in addition, it may be possible to combine some of them. Computer assisted programming may be used instead of the manual approach, especially for complex continuous-path operations, but these are the basic steps involved in both point-to-point and contouring control; see also block diagram of Figure 1–4.

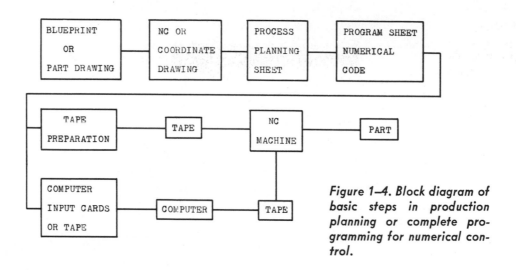

Figure 1–4. Block diagram of basic steps in production planning or complete programming for numerical control.

The foregoing is a brief description only and details will follow in later chapters.

The tape may be prepared on a tape punch or on a standard automatic perforating typewriter such as a Flexowriter, Figure 1–5, as made by Friden, Inc. A punched tape as well as a printout of the tape information are produced automatically as the commands for a program are typed out on this machine. The unit will also reproduce tapes and printouts on an automatic basis.

Low and Medium vs. High Volume Production

Numerical control is basically intended for short and medium runs, rather than for high volume production, although it is also being adapted to the latter. (The term "mass production" is a misleading and inaccurate one, and will not be used here as a regular expression.)

High volume production (as in the automotive industry) requires special tooling and special-purpose production equipment to bring down the cost per part. The initial high capital cost of the special tooling and equipment is justified by the lower production cost per part produced. Such initial costs are not justified, however, for short and medium runs up to 25, 50, or 500 parts. That is where numerical control comes in. Very little if any special tooling is required for an NC machine, which is ready to go to work almost as soon as the tape is prepared; therefore costs per part are lower for short and medium runs.

Moreover, the conventional, high production tooling and equipment are designed to produce only one or a few types of different parts. An NC machine, however, such as a machining center, is designed to handle a wide variety of parts and operations. Further, changeover from one type of part to another is rapid with numerical control, requiring only a change of tapes and standard tooling.

Another comparison of NC machine tools is with conventional, general-purpose machine tools which are also intended for shorter runs, and they are distinct from the high-production machines or production lines. The advantages of using numerical control, however, reduce the costs per part compared with the use of conventional or manually operated general-purpose machines.

Runs of small and medium lots, rather than high volume production or long runs, are the order of the day for many sectors of the manufacturing industry, certainly for most areas in metalworking manufacturing. This is readily apparent in the majority of plants, and is also shown by the following:

1. When the American Society of Tool and Manufacturing Engineers conducted a survey on automation, it established that only 10% of all manufacturing in the metal-working industries in the United States fell or could fall in the high volume category. By far, most of the production was in the small and medium lot field, and this continues to hold true.

Figures 1–5 & 1–6. At left: Using an automatic perforating typewriter, a Flexowriter, for tape preparation, symbolic of the tape approach to numerically controlled manufacturing. (Friden, Inc.) At right: The dial input approach to numerical control, which employs no tape, shown used on a DeVlieg precision boring and milling machine. (DeVlieg Machine Company.)

2. In an estimate by a major machine tool builder, the average size of production lots was 15 to 50 pieces in about 75% of all metalworking manufacturing in the United States.

3. Similarly, another large builder has pointed out that more than 75% of industrial manufacturers make products in lots of 25 parts or less.

4. In any case, probably not more than 35% to 55% of all metalworking and allied manufacturing industries engage in production involving thousands of parts per run. These long runs could in many cases apply only to some of the parts produced by these industries, and not to all of their production.

How to Acquire Numerical Control in Economic Stages

The cost of a numerical control system may constitute 25% to 50% of the entire price of an NC machine tool, depending on the complexity of the work that the numerical control and machine combination is expected to perform. System cost may exceed machine cost.

Several different NC systems, in addition to numerical tape control, are built, and they are often available from the same machine tool or systems manufacturer. They embody varying degrees of sophistication, which are reflected in the price and of course in the capability of the system or NC machine. In order to examine these briefly at this stage, reviewing manual operation of a machine tool first will help to place them in perspective.

FACETS OF MANUAL OR CONVENTIONAL OPERATION

In ordinary manual operation of a machine tool or other production machine, the tool and work positioning motions are carried out manually by the operator, with the assistance of power feeds if necessary. To do this positioning, he uses the graduated feed screws and other measuring aids which are part of the machine tool.

He also adjusts the controls for the correct speeds and feeds to be used in cutting, and then performs the machining operation with the automatic feeds provided on the machine. The operator may also have to set table stops or limit switches to control the length of a cut, as in milling. In other words, the data input is completely manual and takes place directly at the machine's own feedscrews or positioning elements and operating controls.

This approach in manual operation takes care of straight-line cuts, arcs, circles, and other regular geometrical patterns readily cut with power feeds, using the machine tool with accessories if necessary.

It is different when irregular or contoured shapes must be produced by machining. Continuous control over the cutting tool's path, or that of the workpiece, is necessary, and in the absence of numerical control, this is usually accomplished with tracer control. (In tracing or copying, a stylus following the contour of a template or model guides the tool to reproduce the contour on the workpiece. Other control methods will come up in the chapter on alternatives to numerical control.)

In conventional manual operation, the operator also uses numerical data—but these are not in coded form. They are mathematical values, or direct dimensional data. This must necessarily be so, as the dimensions and forms of a part, as specified and shown on the print, are expressed in inches or millimeters, degrees and other measures which serve to dimension and geometrically define the part. The same data is again used for inspecting the finished part.

Under numerical control, the positions, dimensions and contours are obtained automatically, fully or in part, depending on the type of system selected and the mode of operation.

MODES OF OPERATION WITH NC MACHINES

Various numerically controlled machine tools can be operated according to any one of three different, main modes:

1. Manual or conventional operation, usually through manual control of the powered positioning devices provided. ("Manual operation" in some cases means to select a small group of commands on the tape, for an individual operation, and then perform the operation under tape control.)

2. Operation by the dial input type of numerical control, which can also be of push button type instead.

3. Operation under tape numerical control, with the degree of automation selected as required.

OPERATION BY DIAL OR PUSHBUTTON NUMERICAL INPUT

This type of system, sometimes referred to as "manual numerical control," but which will here be termed dial input or dial input numerical control, is employed for point-to-point control and can cost considerably less than a tape control system.

The digits of the numbers representing the coordinates for positioning the workpiece or machine slide, are simply fed into the system by adjusting or setting dials on the control panel or using push buttons as provided. Here the numerical input is manual, but the actual positioning is then carried out automatically by the control system; therefore, no tape is used with this dial input, or manual digital input.

The general arrangement of such a system is shown in Figure 1–6. This is a DeVlieg precision boring and milling machine with dial input numerical control for positioning work, by DeVlieg Machine Company. The coordinate dimensions for positioning the table, and the spindle slide on the column, are dialed in directly from a blueprint or drawing. Positioning then takes place automatically when pressing a push button. The machine is used for precision production work as well as for jig boring or similar tool work.

Various machine tools may be purchased with dial input only or with dial input and tape control combined, as desired. The dial input type of numerical control has sometimes been called "the poor man's numerical control." Its existence, together with choices in the degree of automation provided by tape control, makes it possible to tailor numerical control requirements to suit the economics and production requirements of the individual plant. Dial input, however, obviously lacks some of the advantages of tape control.

With a dial input system, as with many tape controlled systems, an additional visual digital readout may be provided in point-to-point or positioning control. As each position is reached, the digits of the numbers appear on the readout or visual display panel, showing the actual position.

OPERATION BY TAPE INPUT

Whether of point-to-point or contouring type, tape control systems are available with varying degrees of automation and sophistication, affording a choice of additional or special features at the same time. Cards are used instead of tape in some cases (and in computer assisted programming).

Other Automatic Control Methods for Machines

In the foregoing general descriptions of basic numerical control systems, comparisons have not yet been made with earlier as well as with other existing types of automatic controls.

In the machine tool field, automation *per se* is not new, but numerical tape control and the concept behind it are relatively new, when long periods of time are considered.

AUTOMATICS

Automatic screw machines have been used for many years, also other automatic machine tools such as automatic lathes or automatic bar and chucking machines, and many more. Most automatics have relied on cams and associated mechanical devices for their control of operating functions and sequences. Electrical switching to provide automatic cycles for machine functions came later, sometimes employing the cam principle, and interposing electrical control.

TRANSFER MACHINES AND LINES

Transfer lines as in automotive plants, for high volume production of engine blocks, cylinder heads, crankcases and other components, have been developed to a high degree of efficiency, and they operate automatically. (However, some transfer lines have come under numerical control where frequent changeovers are necessary to accommodate greater variety and more limited runs.)

In addition, there are the various forms of special-purpose machine tools, designed for high volume production of specific parts only, or, with modification, for families of similar or closely related parts.

GENERATIONS OF NUMERICAL CONTROL

Numerical control—and the term will be used in these pages generally to indicate tape control, except where collective statistics are given, and unless otherwise stated or evident— has become thoroughly established. Machine tool builders have produced even more generations of numerically controlled machine tools, many designed and built for numerical control from the ground up. Advanced and revolutionary machine tool designs can be incorporated in NC machines, as it is not necessary to adapt the machine to the operator and the process, but largely to the process itself. For example, no conventional operator controls such as handwheels and levers need be provided.

In addition to its use in such advanced machine types, including machining centers, numerical control has been added to a great variety of more common machine tools. This is usually done in the plant of the machine tool builder—the system is "built in"—but field installations are also possible, in which an NC system is added to and made compatible with an existing machine. The latter procedure is known as retrofitting.

The main reasons for adopting numerically controlled manufacturing are:

1. *It provides flexible automation adaptable to many different requirements, and changeovers from one job or setup to another are rapid.*
2. *Numerical control places machine operation and production directly in the hands of management, through the predetermined punched tape or similar program.*
3. *It makes short and medium production runs economical, and can often be used economically even for single pieces. High volume or "mass production" quantities are not required for its economic application.*
4. *Any of these additional advantages may be paramount for an individual plant in adopting NC manufacturing: reduction in lead time, to allow an early start in production; reduced tooling costs in machining operations; lower inspection and assembly costs due to improved uniformity of product; greatly increased machine utilization times; and other factors.*

The nature of numerical control and its additional advantages:

1. *Numerical control provides automatic or semiautomatic operation of machine tools, of other production equipment and processes, and the degree of automation can be selected as required.*
2. *The numerical input or instructions to the control system can be in such forms as punched tape, punched cards, magnetic tape, and manual "dial" or digital input.*
3. *The two main types of numerical control are positioning or point-to-point control, and contouring or continuous-path control.*
4. *Programming an NC manufacturing operation includes both conventional and new steps. Programming can be manual or computer assisted.*

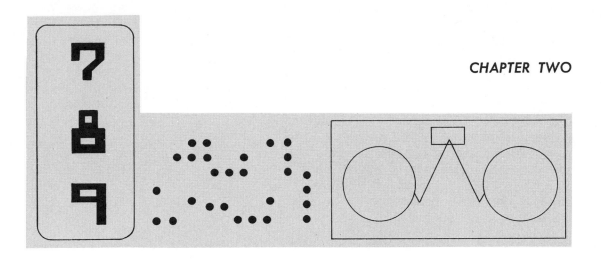

CHAPTER TWO

THE ADVANTAGES OF
NUMERICAL CONTROL

THE ADVANTAGES OF NUMERICAL CONTROL CANNOT BE LISTED READILY IN THE ORDER OF THEIR IMPORTANCE, BECAUSE THE CONDITIONS AND REASONS FOR ADOPTING THE CONCEPT CAN VARY GREATLY FROM ONE PLANT TO THE NEXT.

ONE COMPANY MAY BASE ITS DECISION TO PURCHASE NUMERICALLY CONTROLLED EQUIPMENT CHIEFLY ON THE GREATLY SHORTENED LEAD TIME, THE TIME REQUIRED TO START ACTUAL PRODUCTION OF A PART OR PRODUCT, WHICH IS A SALIENT FEATURE OF THIS MANUFACTURING CONCEPT. SHORTENED LEAD TIME STRENGTHENS THE COMPETITIVE ABILITY OF A COMPANY TO LAUNCH A NEW PRODUCT ON THE MARKET AND TO BID ON CONTRACTS.

ANOTHER COMPANY MAY WANT NUMERICAL CONTROL TO BUY AUTOMATION FOR SHORT RUNS AT LOW COST, AND STILL ANOTHER MAY CHOOSE IT TO turn out highly complex jobs that are not economical or are almost impossible by conventional methods.

The advantages described here in additional detail apply largely to numerical control by *tape input*. Some of these advantages and savings do not accrue when using the dial input type of numerical control in which digital information is dialed into the control system, and the operation—usually positioning—is automatic from that point. (Each type of numerical control has its own particular characteristics and most suitable fields of application.) The following does not necessarily give the advantages in their order of importance; points stated previously are reviewed briefly or treated more fully.

Flexibility, Management Control

Rapid changeover from one part or production run to another can be made because only a change of tape and a minimum of changes in tooling are required. Also, minor design changes in a product do not involve a complete retooling of the project—a new tape is simply punched, or a section repunched. Production of a tape itself is usually much faster and less costly than modifying existing tooling, or making new jigs and fixtures to accommodate design changes in a part.

In addition, other operational changes, as may be dictated by use, can be readily made on tape and repeated on the same job in the future.

In rapidly developing industries, design changes in products, even if of minor nature, are frequent, especially where competition for the market is severe. Tape control affords a great deal of flexibility to make such changes, and in a relatively short time. In addition, management can plan and control practically the entire operation by placing the program on tape.

Advantages of Reduced Lead Time

The appreciable reduction in lead time makes it possible to place a product on the market at the most critical or opportune time. The lead time that is saved also has a substantial dollar value, because it represents actual time spent in profitable production rather than in planning, preparation and tooling.

LEAD TIME SAVINGS THROUGH REDUCED TOOLING

Fewer special tools need be designed and made. The initial layout and making of templates, as required for copying or tracing, are eliminated. Many special gages, jigs and fixtures, which mean many hours of design time and often reflect thousands of dollars in toolmaking, are largely eliminated.

In the case of tracing from simple templates, however, the advantage of numerical control may be slight, and its use may not be indicated. It is different, however, when complex three-dimensional models or masters for tracing, as in die sinking, and templates for more complex contour milling are required for tracer machining. These operations usually lend themselves better to numerical control. The templates or masters themselves may be made by numerical control, instead of by the usual methods involving considerable layout, trial cuts, and a great deal of hand finishing and measuring.

EARLIER DELIVERY AND CONTRACT FULFILLMENTS

Shortened lead time also means earlier and on-time deliveries of replacement parts and inventory requirements. Savings in lead time may range up to 75% or even higher.

Low Cost Automation for Short Runs

Making short runs profitable is always a problem with conventional machining methods, and most metalworking manufacturing is in short to medium production runs.

CONVENTIONAL SHORT RUNS COSTLY

If one part only must be made in the usual way, it is practically a handmade product: the machinist or operator must position and reposition his cutting tools or work table to obtain the various dimensions; he must make corrections, measure, and make further corrections after trial cuts, until the desired dimensions and shapes are obtained.

If a dozen parts are to be made, the procedure is still largely the same. Making special tooling to speed up the work, even of limited nature, may not be economical.

Although the parts run off after the first one are produced faster, the cost per piece is still relatively high, due to the time involved both in the setup and operation of the machine. In addition, spoiled work from short manual runs is almost inevitable, which adds to the cost per part, even if some of the parts can be reworked later. The costs multiply when precision machining is involved. It is in short to medium runs where numerical control can often save the situation and make the whole operation more profitable, or make it possible in the first case.

If parts, however, are to be produced in long runs, in the thousands, then conventional automatic machines can be resorted to instead. These include automatic screw and bar machines, automatic bar and chucking lathes, special-purpose machines, and other automated equipment. Nevertheless, numerical control is also invading the higher volume field in some cases.

PROFITABLE SHORT RUNS WITH NUMERICAL CONTROL

What is a profitable run for a numerically controlled machine? The Woodward Governor Company of Rockford, Illinois, with considerable manufacturing experience behind it, showed that after having about 200 parts programmed, that the runs ranged from five-piece orders to lots as large as 150 parts. Most orders involved only 25 to 50 pieces.

This machining at Woodward Governor ranged from the simple drilling of many holes in some components to the machining of more complex parts involving combinations of drilling, boring, milling and tapping.

The work was carried out on a Cleereman Spindlemaster, a numerically controlled vertical spindle machine which can automatically select any one of 30 tools on tape command, and which provides automatic positioning through tape control of three axes. In addition, its numerical system also controls speeds and feeds, activates the coolant cycle, and performs additional functions. The machine, by Cleereman Machine Tool Corporation, as equipped with General Electric Mark Century numerical control, is shown in Figure 2–1.

In another example, but using dial input this time instead of tape, a cast iron machine tool housing had to be machined in lots of single parts, while other orders consisted only of two pieces to be machined. These involved precision locating to plus or minus 0.001 in. or less (the machine used was designed for a locating or positioning accuracy of 0.0001 in. per foot), and the diameters had to be within 0.0005 in. This work, including additional operations, was performed on a DeVlieg Jigmil, a precision horizontal boring and milling machine by DeVlieg Machine Company.

Further data on what constitutes an economical run for numerical control, and on-the-job examples of manufacturing operations, is given in the chapter on case studies and elsewhere through the book.

Savings in Tool Costs, Tool Storage

Special production tooling is eliminated or greatly reduced when using numerical control. Drilling jigs are usually bypassed entirely, in drilling with point-to-point positioning systems, or when using other end-cutting tools which otherwise require guiding into position through a jig bushing.

Drill jigs must accurately locate the workpiece as well as guide the drills or cutting tools to the correct locations in the work; therefore, they incur considerable toolmaking costs in addition to design costs, except for the most simple types.

The fixture or work holding devices used in milling and other machine operations under numerical control can be very simple.

SAVINGS FROM REDUCED STORAGE, HANDLING, IDENTIFICATION

A large reduction in tooling, together with reductions in such other tools at templates or masters, also results in reduced storage space requirements for these tools, an important saving in itself.

In addition, the handling problem of transporting tools to and from the machine is reduced to a minimum when tape is used. Tape reels are conveniently handled and easily stored, as are punched cards, and require little storage space. Not only is such saved storage space worth money, but the elimination of many special tools does away with numerous hidden costs in record keeping and handling.

Since all production tools must be properly identified, and identification often varies only slightly, confusion with jigs and fixtures alone has sometimes caused the loss of thousands of dollars in the minor point of ordering out such tools for production runs. Difficulties are compounded when identification had not been properly made in the first instance. Practically all of these difficulties are lessened or avoided with tape.

TOOL INSPECTION COSTS DECREASED

When tooling up for a new product, all the jigs, fixtures, gages and other tools must be inspected, and in some cases rework is necessary before they can be accepted for production. With numerical control, however, most of these points are taken care of by the tape itself, as the fixture or work holding device is relegated mainly to holding the work rather than providing elaborate locating and/or guiding facilities as well.

In continuous-path control, the cost of making templates or masters for tracing or copying is avoided.

EXAMPLES OF SAVINGS

Savings as high as 80% over conventional operation, in large measure due to elimination of special fixtures and templates, can be realized in many turning applications, according to studies by Monarch Machine Tool Company, Sidney, Ohio.

The Monarch examples dealt with profile turning by punched tape, instead of using either form tools or the tracing process. In the latter case the templates were replaced by punched tape. Form tools, which produce a profile or desired outline by having the required contour on the cutting edge, frequently result in considerable toolmaking expense, as they must usually be made to order for the individual job. Standard tooling, includ-

Figures 2–1 & 2–2. At top: Used economically on short runs of 5 to 150 pieces, this type of drilling and milling machine has 30 tools available under numerical control from rotary automatic tool changer above spindle. (Cleereman Machine Tool Corp.) At bottom: Tooling costs were cut by 90 percent with this B & S Turr-E-Tape numerically controlled turret drill; machine control unit is shown at left.

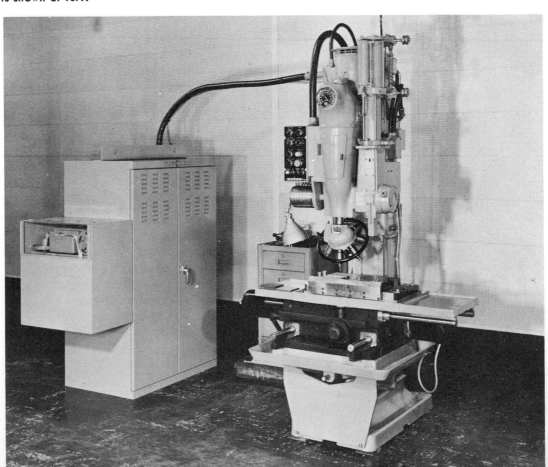

ing standard cutting tools, usually suffices with tape and other forms of numerical control.

In one installation, involving a turret drilling machine, one fixture replaced 19 others, and the company reported that tooling costs were cut 90% on short runs of 100 varied parts. (A return of 45% on capital investment was also stated to be realized in this instance.) The work was performed on a Turr-E-Tape, six-spindle turret drilling machine. An overall view of such a drill, made by Brown & Sharpe Manufacturing Co., appears in Figure 2–2.

Savings in fixturing gained by the Woodward Governor Company in the operations mentioned previously, were estimated at $7,000 in the first year. The company pointed out that this saving was low because a lot of the parts already had fixtures. These fixtures were stripped for the numerical control or NC operations and were then used as simple holding fixtures.

TOOL SAVINGS FROM A NUMERICALLY CONTROLLED TRANSFER LINE

When the Construction Equipment Division of International Harvester Company installed a new engine cylinder block line that was almost completely tape controlled, it made a precedent-setting decision in applying numerical control to a transfer line. This line included 13 tape or numerically controlled machines, one being an 11-station transfer machine regarded as unique in the industry (see Chapter 4 on Case Studies). Figure 2–3 shows this machine, made by Le Maire Machine Tool Co.

Traditionally, transfer lines, in which a series of special machine tools or work stations are connected, have relied on their own form of automation. The work passes automatically

Figure 2–3. An outstanding application of numerical control, this 11-station Le Maire transfer machine helped solve the problem of machining a variety of engine blocks at Melrose Park Works of IHC. (Le Maire Machine Tool Co.)

from one station to the next, making possible the high production necessary for the automotive industry, which is the chief exponent for the transfer line concept.

At the IHC plant at Melrose Park, Illinois, the Division was already producing some 14 models of diesel engines when the company developed a new line of V-type diesels. This step would have required a new production line of conventional type.

Instead, to save high tooling costs and costs of special-purpose machine tools for the transfer line, the company turned to numerical control. It installed a new type of production line for turning out both V-type and in-line blocks with about 40 machines, instead of a line that would have required 65 machines had it been intended to produce both V-types and in-line engine blocks as well. Flexibility, savings in machine costs, in jigs, fixtures, and in perishable tools, were the main criteria in this decision.

With the new line, frequently only simple clamps were necessary instead of special fixtures. Also, fewer cutting tools were needed, because the work was shuttled into precise position under tape command with relation to the cutting tool, and these fewer tools were applied in repeat patterns.

Except for a few final critical operations, this IHC line accommodated all blocks through the same fixtures with only simple alterations. Tooling and tapes were readily changed when switching from one type of engine block to another. The company reported that perishable tool inventory was less than one-fifth than that of conventional transfer lines.

Increased Machine Utilization and Production

The increase in production gained from the use of numerically controlled machine tools and other metalworking equipment is due chiefly to increased machine utilization. The machine is cutting or making chips practically all of the time, with down time reduced to a minimum.

UP TIME MAY REACH 95%

"Up time," the time that the machine is actually working productively, often becomes as high as 85 to 95%. For example, on a Hughes-equipped three-axis Burgmaster turret drill, up time was figured as high as 94%.

Actual cutting speeds for machining, however, are generally not increased, as they are usually determined by the work material, cutting material and other job conditions. Nevertheless, there are cases where such improvements can be made.

Production efficiency was increased 40%, for example, in representative operations on a DeVlieg Jigmil precision horizontal boring and milling machine using numerical control. In these applications, dial input was employed, and with tape (optionally available for the same machine), it should be even faster. These jobs involved cast iron gear housings for machine tools, requiring precision locating and boring.

In general, NC machine tools have production capacities about three times those of conventionally operated ones.

Savings Through Reduced Setup Time

The large reduction in setup time accounts for a major share of the substantially improved machine utilization time. The International Harvester Company, in its NC transfer line, has reduced setup time by 75% or more.

SIMPLIFIED SETUP PROCEDURES

The simple fixtures used with most numerically controlled machining make work holding or clamping a simple matter when making setups for a variety of drilling, milling, boring, and additional operations. With point-to-point control, the setting of table limit stops or dogs, or limit switches and positioning devices, is eliminated entirely, and the operator does not have to depend on feedscrew dials when setting up.

With numerical control, the operator simply "zeroes in" on the reference point of the work for the initial positioning to align the work and tool, and the tape takes over from there. Setting up of cutting tools is simpler also, because standard tools and holders can be used in most operations, instead of the specials used with high production machines, which require more setting.

Setup time in the production of diesel engine parts on vertical turret lathes, for example, has been reduced by as much as 65% on short runs and even single parts.

PRESET TOOLING

To gain the maximum benefit in numerically controlled machining, when exploiting setup time reductions, preset tooling should be used as much as possible (this procedure is dealt with in a later chapter).

More Uniform Quality

An improved product is almost automatic with numerical control. More uniform quality is achieved because all the parts in the series are machined from the same tape, under the same conditions. The cutting speeds and feeds are predetermined, as are all the other factors concerning the operation. Once a tape has been proved and placed into production, errors that can result from manual operation are eliminated.

IMPROVED INTERCHANGEABILITY, REDUCED INSPECTION, FASTER ASSEMBLY

Improvement in uniformity also results from other factors: such as better surface finish, because tape control in itself is more uniform, and tolerances are held more readily. Interchangeability of parts is assured with a minimum of inspection; parts go together better, and hand fitting can be eliminated in the assembly stage.

Many manufactured parts increasingly require 100% inspection, due to more critical service requirements and higher reliability specifications. Such inspection can be reduced considerably with tape controlled parts, and the inspection itself may be carried out under tape control.

Fewer Machines Needed

Drastic reductions are often possible in the number of machines required. A Texas plant which replaced five radial drills with one point-to-point numerically controlled drill is a good example. In the IHC transfer line, as mentioned, only 40 machines were required instead of the 65 under normal transfer line operation.

At the Small Aircraft Engine Department, General Electric Company, West Lynn, Massachusetts, two numerically controlled Sundstrand lathes replaced four previous machines, and the company saved 18 hours on each part in the contour machining of complex spacer rings. The company expected to pay off the machines in less than two years.

At Alco Products, Inc., Auburn, New York, two numerically controlled Sundstrand turret drilling, milling and boring machines, for precision operations on cylinder heads, replaced three multiple-spindle drilling machines, two tapping machines, some radial drilling machines, and a 30-spindle, three-station special-purpose machine tool.

The use of fewer machines means savings in plant space and in shop personnel, a reduction of supervision, and in various cases, reduced capital outlays.

Obsolescence Decreased and Investment Protected

Since numerically controlled machines provide great flexibility in operation, and can perform a wider range of operations than conventionally operated ones, the obsolescence factor is very much decreased. This affords greater protection for the capital invested.

While improvements and changes will continue to be made in numerically controlled machine tools and in the systems themselves, as with all machinery, the fact that a machine is equipped with numerical control makes it less subject to obsolescence than a machine not so equipped.

Operating and Labor Costs Reduced

Reduced operating costs are inherent in the use of NC machines due to the nature of the concept as a whole. Greatly reduced setup times, as already explained, reduce the operating costs. Production increases and direct labor savings in machining on a three-axis turret drill amounted to about 44 percent in one instance.

NUMEROUS FACTORS BRING SAVINGS

As fewer machines are usually required, fewer operators are needed, both for setup and for supplying the machines with stock, and, with semi-automated NC setups, for performing those operations which are left to the operator.

General overhead costs of a plant, which must be considered in establishing a machine-hour rate for a machine's production, are reduced for similar reasons, including fewer servicing and maintenance problems, and lower utility costs such as electric power expenditures.

Tool storage requirements are also reduced to a great extent, as already noted, which contributes to reduced overhead expense. Costs of inspection are cut. There is less rework, if any. Assembly is generally faster and labor costs are lower.

Less supervision is required in all areas, because of the automatic operation and the advance planning. The chances of human errors are reduced and, in some of the most critical areas, practically eliminated.

Some operational savings are more indirect, as described among the further advantages given in this section.

Human Fatigue Factor Reduced or Eliminated

Unlike the operator of a conventional machine tool, a numerically controlled machine can function without becoming "tired," and those functions that may be left to the operator are not likely to induce fatigue. The operator need not take trial cuts, make trial measurements, or make positioning movements. The NC system can also relieve him of tool indexing, or bringing one tool after another into position in proper sequence as with the turret of a turret type drill, or of a turret lathe.

Output as well as quality is the same at the end of a shift as at the beginning. Extra shifts can be run more readily: tape does not become tired.

Tool Life Increased

Longer tool life has been obtained in many numerically controlled machining operations. Cutting tools generally last longer and need regrinding less often. On a Burgmaster turret drilling machine, for example, equipped with a Hughes three-axis system, cutting tool life was improved by as much as 50%.

The Monarch Machine Tool Company has found out that tool life increases from 40 to 60% in numerically controlled lathe operations as a result of the improved control over surface speed. The latter can be controlled accurately under tape, being changed automatically for varying diameters as required. This has a beneficial effect on the cutting edge. The same holds true for the control of cutting feeds.

Increased tool life can also be exploited in a different way as *shortened* tool life, by using higher cutting speeds.

As the result of better controlled cutting speeds and feeds, better surface finishes can be secured.

DECREASED TOOL WEAR WITH JIGS ELIMINATED

With positioning control, drills, reamers and similar tools last longer because they do not have to revolve in a drill jig bushing to guide them, and because drill jigs, such as the box type, are eliminated. The tools run free, there is less wear from chips (chip disposal is a problem with jigs), and they are freely exposed to an ample supply of cutting fluid. Even carbide tools last longer under these conditions.

CUTTING SPEEDS GENERALLY UNCHANGED

Generally speaking, the actual cutting speeds of which a tool is capable, and the cutting feeds, are not increased through the application of numerical control, although there are exceptions.

With good planning, and better control over feeds and speeds—keeping them at optimum values—cutting speeds in some turning operations *have* been increased by 25 to 35%. Ordinarily however, this is not an area in which appreciable savings should be looked for in the application of numerical control. With increased tool life, tolerances are more readily held, and cutting tools need to be changed less frequently, another saving in time.

Reduced Material and Tool Handling

Savings in the handling of materials have been as high as 30%, and may go even higher. In general production, by all types of conventional machine tools, the material handling cost itself may run from 15 to 18% of total cost. Under numerical control, these costs can be reduced considerably.

Instead of moving parts from one machine to another, they are frequently finished on the same numerically controlled machine, with obvious handling steps eliminated. Tool handling is also reduced, as fewer fixtures are required, and frequently this tooling may be adapted readily to several types of similar components, obviating major changes during setups.

Production Schedules Met More Readily, Deliveries Made Faster

Production is planned in the production office rather than on the shop floor as far as the operations on an individual machine are concerned; therefore, it is possible to draw up more exact production schedules. The time required for programming and setting up is more predictable, estimates are less time-consuming than for conventional machine operation, and customer orders for new or replacement parts can be filled faster.

Inventory Can Be Cut, More Quickly Replenished

Lead time is greatly reduced with tape control and production on a part or product can be started without much delay making it possible to cut inventories substantially. This naturally makes for a smaller investment in inventory which represents idle capital. Since the entire program is on tape and it is possible to tool up and set up quickly for production, inventories are more quickly replenished.

Savings from Reduced Supervision and Inspection

In addition to the savings in supervision and inspection already discussed, there are still others.

The elimination of checking *during* machine operation can mean a considerable gain, for example, in vertical turret lathe operation when recessed bores are machined. Trial measurements of dimensions in awkward places or hard-to-reach spots can be eliminated.

Greater Safety in Operation

Increased safety is inherent in numerically controlled machines because operator attention for the various functions is drastically reduced or eliminated. The operator is exposed less frequently to moving machine elements and to cutting tools. There is also greater safety for the machine itself, less danger of damage.

Remote control of machine tools and other equipment is possible. Radioactive materials can be machined under numerical control from a remote station with personnel away from any dangerous radiation. Another important safety factor: less crowding on the plant floor as fewer machines are required.

Research and Development, Prototype Work

When complex models or prototypes must be produced in research or development, this work can often be done more readily by programming the operations on tape or cards instead of using conventional methods.

Complex masters and templates, especially the more involved three-dimensional shapes, are produced by numerical control in the aircraft and missile or aerospace industries, eliminating a great amount of tedious manual work in shop operations. Such tools, and similar intricate parts, can be exactly and mathematically defined for tape programs, making some of these "impossible" jobs practical and economical. Trial and error approaches, numerous trial measurements, corrections, hand finishing and so on, can be dispensed with.

Prototypes in general manufacturing may also call for the use of numerical control, either in making special tooling that may be required, or in making the components themselves.

Savings in Machining from Solid Stock

Both in tool work and in production, the machining of tools or parts from the solid (using stock such as bars, plates, or billets instead of castings or forgings, which provide the initial shape) is effecting many economies.

Automatic forging dies, for example, are made under numerical control on die sinking and three-dimensional contouring machines from solid stock. Much of this work was previously performed under tracer or copying control, and that method is still in wide use where the nature of the template or master is not complex enough to warrant numerical control programming.

In the aircraft industry, wing skins are machined from the solid, instead of being built up from preformed sections. In other industries also, intricate work is produced by this method, instead of building up an assembly or subassembly from separate parts.

Additional But Less Tangible Advantages and Results

Numerical control also provides additional but less tangible advantages. When one or more NC machines are installed in a plant, there is a tendency toward a general upgrading of production practices on the conventional machines in the entire plant. Since the operations are planned more accurately for tape programming, and in greater detail than when conventional production methods are used, the introduction of numerical control leads to a more critical examination of the conventional approaches and subsequent improvements in them.

When fixtures and special tools must be shipped back and forth between subcontractor or branch and main plant, the reduced amount of tooling also saves in shipping and handling charges.

With automation made profitable on short runs, the smaller manufacturer is better able to compete with the larger one who uses high production, special-purpose machine tools for long runs. Any manufacturer, large or small, is in a better position to produce limited quantities of specialty products on an economical basis. Economic lot sizes become smaller and sometimes the economic lot or batch is a single piece.

Communicating Production Programs

Tape or cards can be readily mailed or shipped to a branch plant or subcontractor at a considerable distance to produce interchangeable parts there. Numerical control data can also be transmitted by Teletype and additional methods of communicating over long distances.

Estimating Costs Reduced

With numerical control, the estimating of costs on new production jobs becomes easier and is simplified still more for repetitive jobs. Firm quotations can be made more readily, as management has more complete control over the entire production operation.

Managing the More Complex or "Impossible"

Work which was practically impossible to perform before, especially from the economic standpoint, is frequently made possible and economical by programming it on tape. Examples of the techniques employed have already been quoted—machining from the solid, the production of highly complex masters or templates, the making of other intricate tooling, the mathematical definition of contours and their subsequent production by continuous-path control—and other methods are described throughout the book.

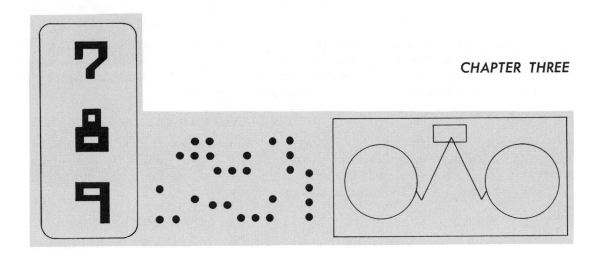

CHAPTER THREE

BASIC TYPES
OF SYSTEMS

System Types

THE BASIC TYPES OF NUMERICAL CONTROL SYSTEMS, ALREADY BRIEFLY OUTLINED IN CHAPTER 1, ARE THE POINT-TO-POINT OR POSITIONING TYPE, THE CONTOURING OR CONTINUOUS-PATH TYPE, AND THE COMBINATION FORM OF SYSTEM, CAPABLE OF BOTH POINT-TO-POINT AND CONTOURING OPERATIONS.

POSITIONING CONTROL

THE MOST FREQUENTLY USED TYPE IS POSITIONING CONTROL, IN WHICH THE CONTROL SYSTEM POSITIONS THE MACHINE TABLE AND THE WORKPIECE ALONG WITH IT, RELATIVE TO THE CUTTING TOOL. THE LATTER MAY BE A DRILL, BORING TOOL, TAP, REAMER, OR A TOOL FOR SOME OTHER OPERATION. AFTER THE HOLE HAS BEEN DRILLED OR OTHER OPERATION PERFORMED AT THAT POINT, THE CONTROL SYSTEM AUTOMATICALLY MOVES THE TABLE TO THE NEXT POINT OR POSITION WHERE ANOTHER

29

hole is to be drilled or another operation performed. Accurate locating and spacing of holes is readily accomplished under numerical control. It relieves the operator of these positioning functions. The addition of feed-rate control, or straight-cut control, makes it possible to take straight-line milling cuts, for example, with positioning systems.

CONTINUOUS-PATH OR CONTOUR CONTROL

In continuous-path control, which is used for producing irregular forms or profiles, as in contour milling, and in three-dimensional machining like die sinking, the path of the cutter is under continuous control. The action of the numerical control system in this case may also be regarded as a *continuous* positioning action.

OTHER SYSTEMS, INPUT DATA

In the third type of system, either point-to-point positioning or contouring may be carried out. There are also some basic variations of these three systems, as will be shown later. Still another type is the functional or cycle control, in which machine functions, rather than positions, are controlled. Machine cycles, speed and feed changes, and other functions, are then controlled by tape. However, on most numerically controlled machines, this functional control is included with positioning or contouring control.

Numerical control systems may also be classified as to digital or analog type. In a digital system, the command signals given out by the control system are of digital or discrete type—they are separate or individual pulses. In an analog system, the command signals are continuous type. Both digital and analog principles may be combined at one point or another in a system.

Digital systems are widely used for both point-to-point and contouring systems, but in earlier stages of development, digital command signals were used chiefly with point-to-point systems, and analog signals were associated with continuous-path or contouring control.

Another classification method for systems is by input: punched-tape or cards, magnetic tape, dial or pushbutton input, initial manual operation and simultaneous recording of machine motions, and "plugboard" or "pegboard" switching—related to but not necessarily numerical control as such. These input types are described further in various chapters.

Punched-tape and cards, as input data, have generally been associated with digital and analog systems, and magnetic tape with analog systems, but these distinctions no longer hold true. Magnetic tape was earlier used extensively with contouring systems in the aircraft industry. Punched-tape has become the chief input medium for most NC machines built in the United States, but magnetic tape continues to be used as well, and in new forms.

Basic Elements

The basic or main elements of a tape operated numerical control system are shown in the block diagram of Figure 3–1. The basic principles here are the same for positioning and contouring, although the latter are somewhat more complex. The following are general explanations; more details will be given in later chapters.

THE TAPE READER

The coded instructions on the tape are first read by the tape reader for conversion by the machine control unit—the heart of the system—into command signals for the appropriate machine movements or functions. The photo Figure 3–2, by American SIP Corporation,

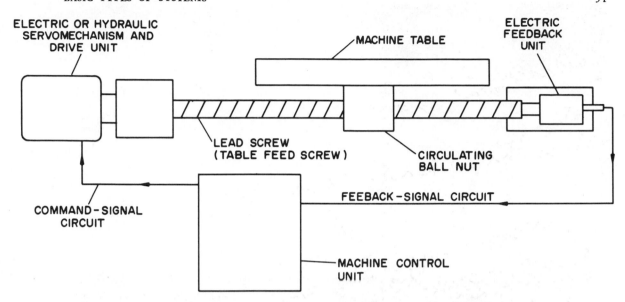

Figure 3–1. Schematic diagram showing basic elements of a tape operated numerical control system.

shows a tape reader and cabinet as used with a numerically controlled Swiss-built Hydroptic SIP machine for precision boring, jig boring, and precision milling operations.

The tape reader is generally mounted in the control console or machine control unit; it may be of electro-mechanical, electronic, pneumatic or optical type. With electro-mechanical operation, fingers or other devices make electrical contact through the holes of the tape; electronic and optical reading make use of photoelectric cells (phototubes or phototransistors), and in pneumatic operation, jets of air are passed through the holes.

Magnetic tape is read by means of a magnetic pickup or scanner, in a method which is similar to that of the conventional tape recorder playback principle.

THE MACHINE CONTROL UNIT

The machine control unit, variously known also as machine control console and machine director, is the center of the whole control system. It may be compared, approximately, with the control switchboard of a telephone exchange system. It accepts the instructions from the tape reader, converts them into the necessary command signals, and transmits the signals to the machine as required. The command signals, which may be in the form of pulses, can produce machine movements of as little as 0.0002 in. to a pulse. Alternatively, command signals may be of analog (continuous) nature, and of a degree of accuracy as required.

The machine control unit is generally not regarded as a computer, although most numerical control systems incorporate some computer circuits. However, the more sophisticated contouring systems have machine control units or directors which are essentially process computers.

SERVOMECHANISM

From the machine control unit, the signals proceed via the command-signal circuit to the servomechanism and drive unit. Each machine slide or movement that is to be controlled by the system has its own servomechanism and drive.

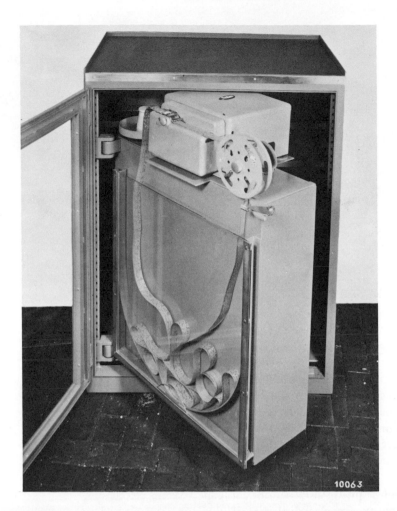

10063

Figures 3–2 & 3–3. At left: A tape reader and cabinet as used with a numerically controlled Hydroptic SIP machine for precision boring, jig boring, and allied milling operations. (American SIP Corp.) At bottom: Closeup of a visual position display panel or readout on a P & W numerically controlled jig borer. (Pratt & Whitney Co., Inc.)

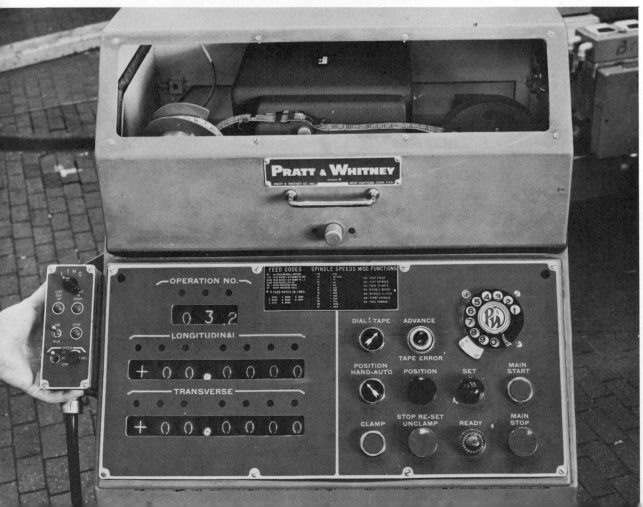

A servomechanism amplifies the incoming signal and provides power to move the necessary machine table or carry out a mechanical movement as required. Commonly, it can be electric or hydraulic. The servomechanism may be an electric motor which drives a machine table through a leadscrew; or, the system may involve hydraulic motors, hydraulic rams, or other devices for moving the controlled machine elements or slides as required. Motors may drive the slides through low-friction leadscrews employing circulating ball nuts or through pinion-and-rack arrangements; or, still other devices can be employed.

THE CONTROLLED MACHINE ELEMENT OR MACHINE TOOL

This is any controlled part of the machine, or the controlled machine itself. It can be an addition to a machine tool; such as a retrofit positioning table or a conversion, but the controlled unit must be designed for numerical control in any case.

FEEDBACK UNIT

The machine motion, as provided through the servomechanism, is recorded or monitored by a feedback (measuring) unit, which may be electric, mechanical, optical, or of some other form. It may be a recording or measuring device, which indicates the position that a machine table or slide, or other motion, has reached in response to tape command.

The feedback unit transmits position signals through the feedback-signal circuit back to the machine control unit, where the signals are continually compared with the command or programmed signals; corrections are automatically made by the machine control unit.

Systems with feedbacks, as in this case, are generally classed as closed-loop types, whereas open-loop systems do not incorporate feedback.

In the operation of a two-axis positioning system, as applied to an upright drilling machine for example, the table or machine slide is automatically locked in place when a desired position has been reached. The operator then performs the drilling operation at that position (unless the machine has been completely automated with numerical control, in which case the operator's attention is not required). He then pushes a button to initiate the positioning cycle for the next hole or position, and so on, until the job is completed.

Extending numerical control to more axes and functions (more machine movements, functions and operations) reduces or eliminates remaining operator functions, depending on the degree of automation desired.

In continuous-path or contouring control, the operator normally need not exercise any controlling function once the cutter has started on its programmed path under numerical control.

VARIATIONS AND ADDITIONAL ELEMENTS

A visual readout panel is a very useful additional feature on a point-to-point system. Numbers, usually on a lighted panel, appear and indicate the positions which have been reached on (or programmed for) the machine axes. This serves as a visual check on the position and assists the operator in determining the stage of the job's completion.

Figure 3–3 shows such a position display panel, as used on a numerically controlled jig borer by Pratt & Whitney Company, Incorporated. A "telephone" type input dial is shown at upper right of panel. The position display indicates the longitudinal and transverse (X and Y axis) positions reached through tape control or by dialing in the coordinates which determine the positions.

Some variations from the basic elements as described above may be noted. In one of the earlier systems (the Numill numerical control system by Autonetics Div., North American

Aviation, Inc.), which was initially developed for toolmaking in the aircraft industry (involving contour milling and drilling of small lots and single-piece quantities), was incorporated an interesting tape reader with a different function from the conventional one.

This tape reader, and some systems continue to use similar aspects, searched and located the required part of a magnetic tape which stored information for producing several hundred different parts. The display panel also had a different function from the usual one. Receiving information from the tape, it indicated the size and kind of material to be used for that particular part or tool, the drill size or size of other cutter, and the speed in revolutions per minute for the drill or other cutting tool to be used on that job. The operator then used these instructions to set up the machine, after which the operation was automatic. Only 12 inches of this tape was required to store all the instructions for producing an average part or tool. The magnetic tape was separate from the control tape, and the latter was produced on a computer. The tools produced included templates, profile mill fixtures and profile bars, all of two-dimensional type.

The Axes or Motions of an NC System

The number of axes or machine motions to which numerical control is applied commonly ranges from two to five, and in special cases goes higher.

The two axes of a representative point-to-point or positioning system are the straight-line movements of the longitudinal and cross or transverse slides, these two machine motions occurring at 90 degrees to each other. They are respectively X and Y axes, and these motions position the workpiece by positioning the table or surface, on which it is mounted, according to rectangular coordinates.

A third axis may be added by applying numerical control to the up and down movement of the spindle of a vertical milling machine or of an upright drill, for example. This becomes the Z axis. These are the usual axis designations. See diagram, Figure 3–4.

In contouring systems, such a third axis provides three-dimensional control—for milling cavities in dies or molds, or for other contour milling in three dimensions.

MACHINE WITH FIVE AXES

The photograph of Figure 3–5 illustrates the application of numerical control to five axes. It shows a five-axis Cincinnati profile miller with horizontal spindle, designed to simplify the machining of complex shapes under numerical control, especially as encountered in the aerospace industry. This machine can cut in five directions simultaneously. The axes are as follows (see also diagram of Figure 3–6):

1. *The X axis is the longitudinal travel of the table on its bed.*
2. *The Y axis in this case is the vertical or up and down travel of the spindle carrier, or milling head carrier, on the column (the rise and fall movement).*
3. *The Z axis is the cross or transverse motion represented by the extension and retraction of the spindle carrier.*
4. *The A axis is a rotary motion of the spindle carrier in the vertical plane.*
5. *The B axis is also a rotary motion, that of the column (on its base) in the horizontal plane.*

Milling an elliptical part with sloping walls, using five axes of the machine at once, and the machining of complex dies, are examples of work the machine can perform automatically under numerical control.

The number of axes used to designate a particular system for numerical control installa-

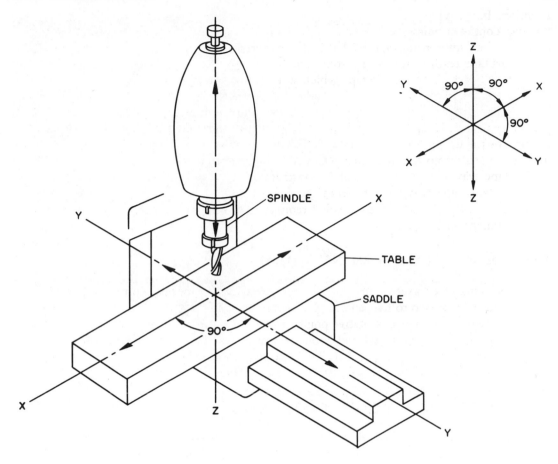

Figure 3–4. Diagram showing the three axes—X, Y, and Z—or longitudinal, transverse, and vertical motions, respectively, as applied to a vertical-spindle machine.

tion does not refer to the number of functions which can be programmed into tape, as these can be quite numerous.

Provision for an automatic tool changer is sometimes regarded as adding another axis to a system, but it is not an axis in the usual positioning sense.

Technical Status of Numerical Control

Numerical control systems have advanced to a point where many now use fully transistorized construction for the control circuits as well as employing modular construction. The latter allows modules or individual units of the circuits in the machine tool control unit or system to be removed with ease for testing or service.

Various special features are available on an optional basis, to allow the user to fit the system to his particular requirements. Most numerically controlled machine tools are designed specifically for numerical control. However, the retrofit principle is still being applied. In such cases, the system, involving a positioning table, for example, is adapted to a machine

Figure 3–5. A five-axis numerically controlled Cincinnati profile milling machine for machining complex forms. (The Cincinnati Milling Machine Co.)

tool which has already been in use for some time or was not originally intended for numerical control. The development of integrated (micro) circuits, following transistorized construction, has further improved reliability and greatly reduced the space required.

Machining or Production Centers

One of the notable developments in NC machine tools has been the emergence of the machining center or production center. This is a multi-purpose, universal type of machine which can perform a great variety of machining operations, all under tape control, and can draw upon a great variety of tools, likewise under tape control.

One model of a Milwaukee-Matic machining center (by Kearney & Trecker Corporation), has 31 different tools available on tape command—30 in the automatic tool changer drum and an additional tool in the spindle, making 961 different tool conditions possible.

The Hughes MT-3 machining center (by Hughes Aircraft Company, Industrial Systems Division), permits the use of 45 different tools in one setup, and automatic tool changes are made in a stated three seconds minus.

The five-axis Omnimil (by Sundstrand Machine Tool), designed for milling, drilling, boring, contour milling and additional operations under numerical control, has an automatic

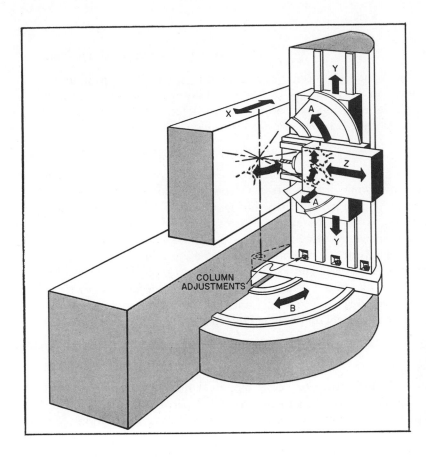

COLUMN
ADJUSTMENTS

Figure 3–6. This schematic drawing shows the five axes of motion of the Cincinnati profile milling machine in Fig. 14. ("Report from Cincinnati Milling," The Cincinnati Milling Machine Co.)

tool changer which accommodates up to 60 different cutting tools. Other production centers are built for sheet and plate punching or fabricating.

Generations of NC Machine Tools

Numerically controlled machine tools which have been developed through a number of generations include milling machines; profile and die sinking milling machines; machining centers; drilling machines including turret drills, turret lathes, and other types. They are designed especially for numerical control application, and are based on much previous experience with machine tools.

An interesting example of a production lathe built for use with numerical control from the ground up is the tape-controlled Numeriturn by The Lodge & Shipley Co. Shown in Figure 3–7, this is a high-duty production lathe with 32-inch swing over the bedways (maximum work diameter), and a 20-inch swing over the cross slide, with a capacity of 336 inches between centers. It is intended to provide a high machine utilization factor—75 to 85% —with 100% machine management. This contrasts with 25 to 30% in many shops when on a conventional basis. A new design of 10-station automatic tool changer, under tape control, is employed.

Overall reliability of all numerical control systems has been improved over a number of years, and programming procedures have been simplified.

Reliability of NC Machines

How reliable in operation are numerically controlled machine tools? The development of numerical control reached the stage some time ago where builders did not hesitate to guarantee satisfaction, as far as a guarantee can be given with any type of production machine. For example, in connection with its Tape-O-Matic drilling machine, introduced in about 1961, Pratt & Whitney included a five-year warranty on defective parts and workmanship, which it claimed to be a "first" for numerically controlled machines.

"DEBUGGING" OF SYSTEMS OR MACHINES

Both builders and users, together with systems manufacturers, have pooled their experiences and knowledge in improving numerical control systems and making them practicable for commercial production. It must be admitted that, during the initial years, considerable "debugging" was often necessary, as could be expected with an entirely new concept of manufacturing, and not all customers were happy.

Some debugging will probably always be necessary, as most new machines of practically any type require some initial adjustments and checks on the job in an individual plant. This problem need no longer be a serious one, and it is now usually resolved in a fairly short time.

Some difficulty should be expected at the beginning, until the shop personnel and everyone concerned become completely familiar with the new concept and details of the machines and systems.

INITIAL TESTING, ORIENTATION PROGRAM

During the past, one large manufacturer of heavy electrical machinery has made it a practice to test all new machine tools first, in a separate, special department, before placing them in production. The plant's machines are tested from the setup, production, and maintenance standpoints.

The manufacturer applied this policy to conventional machine tools long before anyone heard of numerical control. The policy also provides orientation for shop personnel before the machines reach the production floor.

Larger plants may well follow this example for numerically controlled machines. If the operations to be performed are going to be particularly complex, small as well as large shops could profit from such a policy.

STANDARD TAPE AND RELIABILITY

As for general reliability in operation, the programming on standard tape format will also prevent spoiled work and damage to the machine. The 1 in., eight-channel or eight-track (also known as eight-level) tape of the EIA (Electronic Industries Association) standard incorporates the "parity check" concept. An extra hole is punched in the transverse row of holes, to fall within the parity-check channel or track, whenever necessary, so as to always result in an odd number of holes in a transverse row (odd parity-check).

Under this routine, the tape reader can only obtain a false reading (and the machine will stop immediately afterwards) under the following conditions: (1) if the tape has been damaged through improper functioning of the tape-perforating typewriter, or has been mutilated in some other way, and (2) if the tape reader functions improperly. Generally improved programming has also increased reliability and simplicity of operation.

How Accurate are Numerically Controlled Machines?

As one example of accuracy, the Lodge & Shipley Numeriturn lathe already mentioned provides a stated repeatability of positions to within ± 0.0005 in. (plus or minus 0.0005 in.).

Another example is the TRW-3000 contour control system by The Bunker-Ramo

Figures 3–7 & 3–8. At top: Lodge & Shipley's Numeriturn lathe of 32 in. swing, with special design of 10-station automatic tool changer. (The Lodge & Shipley Co.) At right: Modules are readily removed for inspection or maintenance on this machine control unit. (The Fosdick Machine Tool Co.)

Corporation (formerly Thompson Ramo Wooldridge Inc.), which was designed to meet NAS (National Aerospace Standards) specifications. It provides optional or selectable ranges of resolution. These are ± 0.001, ± 0.0001, and ± 0.00001 in., respectively. The values 0.001, 0.0001, and 0.00001 in., also represent the smallest programmable increments. This company has supplied all solid-state (i.e., transistorized) TRW-3000 contour systems since 1959.

The accuracy or degree of precision obtained by the user depends on the accuracy of the system plus the accuracy of the machine tool itself. In a positioning system, this involves both the accuracy of table positioning and that of the repeatability of positioning. An example here is a Burgmaster turret-type drilling machine equipped with Bendix Dynapoint-20 three axis positioning system in which the positioning accuracy as required for the application is given as ± 0.001 in. and the repeatability, for any position, as ± 0.0005 in.

The degree of accuracy required of a numerically controlled machine tool or of other equipment depends on the nature of the machine and the accuracy of the operations to be carried out on it. Additional criteria of numerical control accuracy will be discussed in further chapters.

What are the Factors Affecting Maintenance?

Some of these have already been mentioned—modular and transistorized construction with plug-in module assemblies of solid-state type used extensively, for example, in the TRW-3000 system already noted. Another example is in the Monarch Pathfinder, a numerically controlled lathe which uses modular plug-in printed circuit boards. All such modules or individual units are readily tested, removed from a control circuit and replaced, and this design approach has become practically standard.

Figure 3–8 shows modular construction of a machine control unit, by The Fosdick Machine Tool Company, with a panel of crossbar switches being removed. Systems with electric instead of electronic components use improved relays and other improved electrics.

One of many satisfied users of numerical control, Woodward Governor Company, already mentioned, has succeeded in holding down time to 5 percent. This was achieved by education of its electricians and machine repairmen, the company reported, adding that the down time was divided almost evenly between electrical and mechanical trouble.

Machine tool builders of numerical control equipment provide training for customer personnel, both in operation and maintenance, as well as providing specialized customer service, which should be considered by every prospective buyer and user.

Basic Design that Contributes to Reliability

Numerically controlled machine tools are now generally designed from the outset to be compatible with numerical control, so that the machine and system form an integrated, well functioning unit. Numerous machine tool design improvements have been effected to reduce friction in the slides and actuating members such as the leadscrews or feedscrews.

Particular attention is paid to increasing or providing the necessary degree of rigidity and to reducing vibration, and, factors are taken into account to reduce as much as possible the effects of temperature changes on the machine's accuracy. This is an important point, as a programmed sequence does not lend itself readily to corrections normally made by an operator for any inaccuracies arising from temperature variations, deflection, and so on. Although provisions exist in various NC installations for such compensating adjustments by the operator, such intervention is best held to a minimum.

Various features of the systems themselves contribute to reliability; for example, the visual readout or display panel which, at a glance, gives the operator the position that has been reached after a positioning movement, in a point-to-point system. (Such a readout may instead show the programmed instead of the actual position—it depends on the system.)

How Capital Investment Costs Have Come Down: Examples

1. The Tape-O-Matic drilling machine, already mentioned several times—because it is one of the good examples where the machine tool manufacturer has designed and built a product at a price to suit the user—originally cost $8,595 and up; a similar machine would have cost from $15,000 to $30,000 several years ago.

2. By contrast, the same company's Model PW 1000 numerically controlled jig borer, brought out in 1964, cost $31,995. In a jig borer of average size, the numerical control may add about $18,000 to the cost of the machine tool itself.

3. The price of any NC machine, aside from the marketing and manufacturing policies of the builder, depends mostly on its complexity and size. A simple point-to-point positioning system with two axes may run from $5,000 to $8,000, and a continuous-path system from $60,000 to $90,000.

4. Another example is the nominal investment of $13,945 for a Bridgeport milling and drilling machine with a two-axis numerical control system by Moog Inc., Hydra-Point Division. The system is capable of point-to-point positioning and straight-line milling operations, with table positioning designed for a tolerance of $\pm$ .001 in., and repeatability of position within $\pm$ 0.0003 in.

5. Another precision jig boring, milling and drilling machine of large capacity and advanced design may cost around $152,000, of which about $87,000 would be for the numerical control system (guaranteed accuracy of positioning would be 0.000075 in. (or 75 millionths in.). Jig borers generally reflect the highest degree of precision built into a machine tool.

Jig borers, and combined jig boring, milling and drilling machines, can position work or space holes, and then bore holes, within extremely close tolerances, and their use is not only in the production of tools such as complex drilling jigs but also for a variety of machine housings and other similar components requiring the same degree of precision in such operations.

6. Again, by contrast with regard to prices, tape control for machine functions may add only $6,000 to a single-spindle bar or chucking automatic. Another example, a recent expression of a sophisticated machine tool and system design, representing an investment of about $100,000, would probably have cost almost one and a half times that, five or six years before.

7. Recently developed models of numerically controlled punching equipment cost from under $20,000 to about $40,000.

8. With a trend toward multi-purpose machines, such as machining centers with automatic tool changers, and combined drilling, milling and boring machines with manual tool changing, costs may range from under $80,000 to about $200,000 for the former (and less for turret-type machines) down to less than $20,000 for a three-axis machine, for the latter category. There is a machine type and price to suit practically any requirement.

Other NC Cost Factors

Various features are now made optional on some control systems in order to reduce the cost to the purchaser.

Although costs of the systems have come down from the time they were applied only to contouring control in military applications for the Air Force, and will probably continue to go down, such reductions in prices would only be relative to the prices of machine tools or other capital equipment in general. Prices of both consumer products and machinery have shown a general upward trend over a period of recent years, and this trend may continue for some years to come.

The NC machine tool user may also save on capital investment costs through the additional fact that he will usually require fewer machines compared with conventionally operated ones.

The machine tool builders and control system manufacturers have spent millions of dollars in perfecting numerical control. There is hardly a major machine tool builder today who is not offering it among his machines. Forward-looking management and production men are buying numerical control and putting it to work. The favorable status of numerical control is well established.

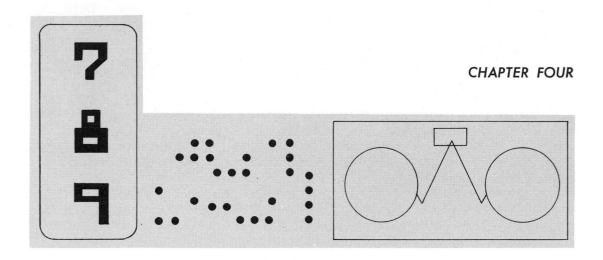

CHAPTER FOUR

CASE STUDIES
OF APPLICATIONS

THE LOT SIZES OF PARTS PRODUCED ON NUMERICALLY CONTROLLED MACHINES RANGE FROM SINGLE PIECES TO THE THOUSANDS, DEPENDING ON THE APPLICATION. SMALL AND MEDIUM LOTS FREQUENTLY FORM THE MOST PROFITABLE RUNS, AS COSTS OF SPECIAL TOOLING ARE ELIMINATED OR GREATLY REDUCED, AND SETUP TIME IS LIKEWISE REDUCED.

SUBSTANTIAL SAVINGS THROUGH LEAD TIME REDUCTIONS, INCREASED PRODUCTION THROUGH HIGHLY IMPROVED MACHINE UTILIZATION TIME, AND REDUCED INSPECTION, ARE A COMMON OCCURRENCE WHEN PROPERLY APPLIED NUMERICAL CONTROL PRODUCTION EQUIPMENT IS UTILIZED. THE FOLLOWING CASE STUDIES DEMONSTRATE THESE SAVINGS.

43

CASE STUDY NO. 1

APPLICATION: *Perform 14 Operations on Coil Supports, on Lathe*
SAVINGS: *74% on Direct Labor*

This case study involves 14 operations with two handlings in the machining of coil supports, which are castings of 60–40–10 ductile iron. A Monarch Pathfinder numerically controlled lathe, equipped with a six-position turret on the carriage, is employed. (See Figure 4–1 for a closeup of a turning operation from the turret, and Figure 4–2 for unmachined and machined coil supports.)

Total Machining Time: 25 minutes, against a former allowed time of 98.5 minutes.

Savings: Direct labor savings of 74% are realized in this case study, which is by The Monarch Machine Tool Co. Saved also are 3 hours of setup time.

Analysis: These lathe operations combine the advantages of a power indexing turret, rapid traverse approach to and from the work, and automatic cycle with tape control. Presetting of tools on the interchangeable turret body also speeds setup.

CASE STUDY NO. 2

APPLICATION: *Drill Part and Spot for Solenoid Ports*
SAVINGS: *$14.00 per Hour of Operation*
POTENTIAL MACHINE PAYOFF: *3¼ Months*

This operation includes drilling all holes on the top face of the part in Figure 4–3, and spotting solenoid ports for location, using point-to-point or positioning numerical control. This study, by Moog Inc., Hydra-Point Division, involves the company's numerical control system as mated with a Bridgeport milling machine (Bridgeport Machines, Inc.). Figure 4–4 shows details of the installation, but with a setup for processing a different component.

Here are the comparisons of the old and new methods:

Previous Method—Using Spindle Drill Presses

Time, 0.61 hr. per piece × $7 per hr. = $4.27
Lot size, 25 pieces
Number per year, 125 pieces × $4.27 .... $ 533.75
Fixture costs, $345.00 .... 345.00
Fixture modification, $95.00 .... 95.00
Setup, 3.5 hr. × 5 × $7 per hr. 122.50

Total $1,096.25

New Method—With Numerically Controlled Vertical Milling Machine

Time, 0.28 hr. per piece × $9 per hr. = $2.52
Lot size, 25 pieces
Number per year, 125 pieces × $2.52 .... $ 315.00
Holding fixture cost—universal vise (standard equipment)
Tape preparation, 3.1 hr. × $12 per hr. 37.20
Engineering changes, 2 hr. × $12 per hr. 24.00
Setup, 2 hr. × 5 × $9 per hr. 90.00

Total $ 466.20

Figures 4–1 & 4–2. At top: Machining coil support casting of Case Study No. 1. (The Monarch Machine Tool Co.) At bottom: Coil support castings of same case study. (The Monarch Machine Tool Co.)

Figures 4–3 & 4–4. At top: Component of Case Study No. 2, drill and spot on top face. (Moog Servocontrols, Inc., Hydra-Point Div.) At bottom: An overall view of a Moog Hydra-Point numerical control system matched with a Bridgeport milling machine. (Moog Servocontrols, Inc., Hydra-Point Div.)

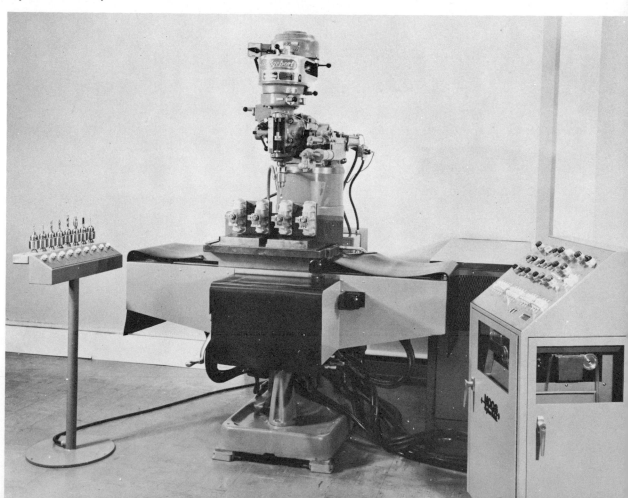

Savings: Actual savings, $630.05, or $14.00 per hour of operation. Machine pay-off period: 3½ months on work as represented by this part, based on two shifts, a 40-hour week and 80% operating or machine utilization time.

Only 11 min. out of every hour are required for operator attention.

Analysis: A substantial saving resulted here by replacing a fixture, eliminating fixture modification, and using a standard universal vise. Tape preparation and setup times together cost approximately the same as the setup time alone under the old method.

CASE STUDY NO. 3

APPLICATION: *Perform 10 Machining Operations on Castings*
SAVINGS: *$13 per Hour of Operation*

A series of 10 machining operations is carried out on a casting, see Figure 4–5, using a Moog Hydra-Point controlled Bridgeport milling machine, similar to that of Case Study No. 2. The operations are carried out with numerical positioning control, together with feed-rate (straight-cut) control.

Figure 4–5. Casting for numerically controlled machining under Case Study No. 3. (Moog Servocontrols, Inc., Hydra-Point Div.)

Operations

1. Face large pad
2. Mill ½ in. × 1/16 in. deep relief

3. Drill ⅜ in. hole through
4. Bore 17/32 in. radial clearance

5. Finish face ¾ in. diameter
6. Countersink at 45 deg.
7. Drill two holes, ¹³⁄₃₂ in.

8. Drill, counterdrill, countersink and ream
9. Drill eight 0.089 holes for tap
10. Countersink

Previous Method—Using Spindle Drills and Vertical Spindle Milling Machines

Time, 0.54 hr. × $7 per hr. = $3.78
Lot size, 90 pieces
Number per year, 900 pieces × $3.78 .... $3,402.00
Fixture costs, three for total of 850.00
Fixture modification, two times 75.00
Setup, 7 hr. × 10 × $7 per hr. 490.00

Total $4,817.00

New Method—Using Numerically Controlled Vertical Milling Machine

Time, 0.225 hr. per piece × $9 per hr. = $2.02
Lot size, 90 pieces
Number per year, 900 pieces × $2.02 .... $1,818.00
Holding fixture costs, right-angle block with dowels 75.00
Tape preparation, 5.5 hr. × $12 per hr. 66.00
Engineering changes, (2) × 1 hr. × $12 .... 24.00
Setup (tools kept set, stored in crib) 2.2 hr. × 10 × $9 per hr. 198.00

Total $2,181.00

Savings: Actual savings, $13 per hour of operation, and the operator's attention is required for only 11 minutes per hour.

Machine Payoff Period: Only 3⅓ months, when machine and system are applied to work as typified by this part. This is again based on two-shift shop operation, a 40-hour week, and 80% machine utilization time.

Analysis: One numerically controlled machine takes the place of several conventional machine tools. The simple holding fixture—a right-angle block with dowels—is less than ¹⁄₁₀ of the orignal cost of the three fixtures used with the previous, conventional method, not counting the fixture modifications required with the latter.

Tolerances in Case Studies 2–3

In the two preceding case studies, the hole and location tolerances range down to a minimum of ± 0.001 in. The majority of these locations have tolerances of ± 0.005 in., which are readily held. Table positioning with the Hydra-Point system is designed to be accurate within ± 0.001 in. absolute. Of course, any looseness in the machine elements such as the spindle—or in the table slides, if the gibs of the latter are improperly set—will affect the accuracy, as will poor cutter and tool grinding. With the proper precautions and reasonable care in setting up, a tolerance of 0.0003 in. should be obtained on hole diameters.

Repeatable positioning accuracy is a stated ± 0.0003 in. (at 72 deg. F). This numerical control system, by the way, is non-electronic. The work table is positioned hydraulically in relation to a mechanical reference point. The punched tape is read pneumatically. The system is suitable for both point-to-point positioning and straight-line milling.

CASE STUDY NO. 4

APPLICATION: *Perform over 260 Machining Operations on Cast Iron Part*
SAVINGS: *Production Time Reduced from 17½ to 3½ Hours*

One of the larger numerically controlled machine tools, equipped with automatic tool changer, as used in this case study by Sundstrand Machine Tool, Division of Sundstrand Corporation, achieved a saving of 14 hours per part. The numerical control method required 3½ hours, compared to the 17½ hours needed by the previous method. The cast iron part is shown in Figure 4–6.

The Machine

The machine used is a Sundstrand numerically controlled, three-axis Model 21 Jigmatic, a multi-purpose machine (machining center) for milling, contour milling, drilling, tapping and many related operations. The automatic tool changer, on a vertical axis, provides 20 positions for automatic tool changing with preset tools, as in Figure 4–7. This is a rail-type machine (having a cross rail between the two vertical columns, adjustable vertically on the column ways).

The machine is equipped with a TRW-3000 numerical control system by The Bunker-Ramo Corporation. The system employs transistors and diodes to provide all solid-state circuits with plug-in module assemblies.

Operations

Nineteen tools used on the Jigmatic machine carry out over 260 operations on this part, including: drilling, chamfering, counterboring, tapping, reaming, and slot milling on both top and bottom. The casting is held on the table in a quick-acting vise.

Savings: Machining time on this part is reduced from 17½ hours to 3½ hours.

Analysis: Several conventional machines are replaced with this NC machine equipped with automatic tool changer. Simplified setups, greatly reduced non-cutting times, simplified and cheaper work holding methods, better and more uniform fits—the latter reducing or eliminating corrections on the assembly floor—made this large gain possible.

CASE STUDY NO. 5

APPLICATION: *Drill, Bore and Contour Mill Pump Wobbler Part*
SAVINGS: *Machining Time Reduced from 30 Hours to 2.5 Hours per Part*

The steel pump wobbler part of this case study is machined from the solid (see blank at left of Figure 4–8). A closeup of the contour milling operation included in this job is shown in Figure 4–9.

This case study, also by Sundstrand Machine Tool, again involves the Sundstrand three-axis Jigmatic machine with 20-position automatic tool changer and TRW-3000 control.

The operations include drilling, boring, and contour milling. The parts are run off in lots of six.

Savings: The previous method, in which the part started out as a forging, required an average of 30 hours per part, and a lead time of some 10 weeks for the forged part approach.

Figures 4–6 & 4–7. At top: Cast iron part for Case Study No. 4 (Sundstrand Machine Tool.) At bottom: Over 260 machining operations are performed with 19 tools, using automatic tool changer. Case Study No. 4. (Sundstrand Machine Tool.)

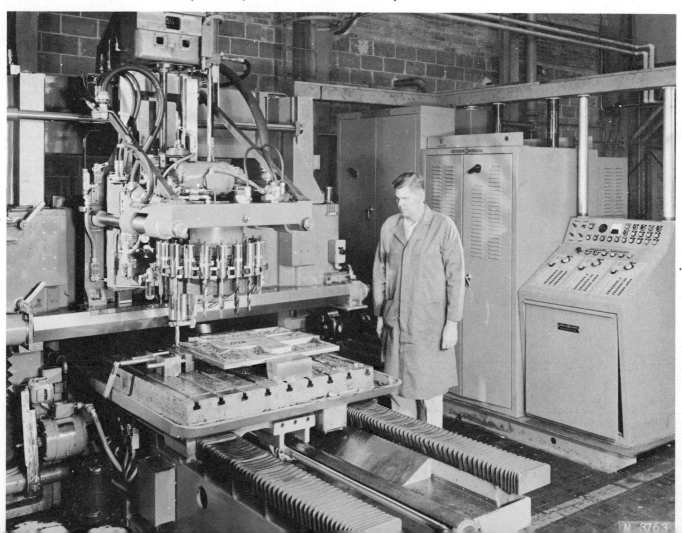

Figures 4–8 & 4–9. At top: Pump wobbler part of Case Study No. 5. From the left: blank, rough-machined and finished parts. (Sundstrand Machine Tool.) At bottom: Closeup of contour milling on steel pump part, Case Study No. 5. (Sundstrand Machine Tool.)

Using numerical control and machining from the solid, production time is cut to 2.5 hours per part from the former 30 hours. Programming and tool preparation take an additional 15 hours, but need not be repeated after the first part is made.

The former, conventional method, was much slower and showed a high scrap rate, because of the close tolerances demanded on this job.

Analysis: These savings also serve to demonstrate the economics of numerical control and its justification on this and similar applications. Machining contours from the solid—using a simple blank instead of an initially preformed shape such as a casting or forging, is simplified by numerical control operation; it eliminates the cost of forgings or castings and speeds up the entire operation.

This is another example of economic short runs of complex shapes, using numerical control: small lots of only six parts at a time are run off in this case.

CASE STUDY NO. 6
APPLICATION: *Automotive Transfer Line for Diesel Engine Manufacture*
SAVINGS: *Numerous! Capital Equipment and Floor Space Requirements are Practically Halved—with 40 instead of 65 Machines in Production Line*

In a radical departure from usual automotive-type transfer line concepts, the Construction Equipment Division of International Harvester Company installed a new diesel engine cylinder block line which is almost entirely tape controlled (see also Chapter 2).

Because the trend in the construction industry is for ever-larger but fewer units in earthmoving machinery, the lower quantities of engine blocks required did not justify the installation of a conventional, high-volume production automotive-type transfer line and the special tools required for it.

Instead, International Harvester decided to install a "general-purpose" transfer line which would handle a variety of engine blocks rather than one type only; the decision was accelerated with the introduction by IHC of a new line of V-type diesel engines which would have required a fourth production line. At the same time, the new line was designed to exploit the efficient transfer line principle (instead of the conventional alternative of utilizing more or less standard, individual machines and on a job-shop basis; the latter approach would have been too slow to meet the engine block requirements). (In all, IHC already had some 14 models of diesel engines before development of the new V-type began.)

Engineers of Le Maire Machine Tool Company, in consultation with IHC, designed and built an 11-station transfer machine, believed to be the first of its kind in the industry. It is outstanding among the 13 tape or numerically controlled machines in the new production line. Machine tools of NC type, by other builders, are also represented in the new line, including units by Kearney & Trecker Corporation, Cleereman Machine Tool Corporation, and The Foote-Burt Company.

The 11-Station, Numerically Controlled Transfer Machine

This 11-station NC transfer machine can automatically process a wide range of engine blocks, including:

- short V-8 engine cylinder blocks
- long V-8 blocks
- V-12 blocks
- 4-in-line blocks
- 6-in-line blocks

This Le Maire transfer machine, shown with an overall view in Figure 4–10, is composed of four fully integrated shuttle machines. The shuttle tables, which "shuttle" or bring the blocks into exact longitudinal positions relative to the cutting tools many times in a cycle, are numerically controlled.

Figure 4–10. General view of precedent-setting 11-station numerically controlled automotive transfer machine by Le Maire Machine Tool Co. at work in International Harvester Company plant. (Viewed from last work station of machine.) (Le Maire Machine Tool Co.)

"Tunnel" fixtures are used, one mounted on the table of each of the four units. The engine blocks are moved from one station to the next by a transfer bar, which passes through the crank bores of the blocks and runs the full length of this transfer machine. There is a separate tape program for each type of engine block. Multiple spindles are used in connection with numerical control, another departure from usual practices. The numerical control system is by Allen-Bradley Company.

The line as a whole, widely uses the concept of bringing the work to the tools, in a series of successive moves, thus requiring relatively few tools, rather than bringing special multiple tooling to bear on the work. This makes for rapid changeovers as required by the shorter production runs, eliminates much extra special tooling, and slashes setup and tooling times.

Although this is not the first example of a numerically controlled transfer machine or line, it is believed to be the first production installation of such a line made by a major automotive equipment manufacturer.

Operations performed on the 11-station NC transfer machine include: rough bore the engine blocks for cylinder sleeves; drill holes in bank faces and between these faces of the blocks; spot-drill and through-drill injector and tappet holes; tap all holes in bank faces and in surfaces between them; and semi-finish ream tappet and injector holes.

When rated at 100% efficiency, this transfer machine processes 4.75 small V-8 or 3.2 large V-8 engine blocks per hour. Because each block is passed through the transfer machine twice, the number of blocks machined in an hour is actually double that of the finished rate. Accuracy of numerically controlled positioning is within 0.0005 in.

Savings: These are too numerous to evaluate here. There is a big reduction in capital investment, also in floor space, since only about 40 machines are required in the new production line instead of the 65 that would normally be required.

Costs of jigs, fixtures and perishable tools are cut to a minimum. Inventory of perishable tools is less than one fifth that of conventional lines. This is because a single tool such as a drill or tap is used to perform a whole series of operations: the workpiece, in this production line as a whole, is successively presented to the tool (instead of using a group of tools at a specific station to perform a number of operations during the same stroke or approach, as in most special-purpose and transfer machines in the automotive field).

Additional savings are in inspection costs: when a single tool, such as a tap, is used to perform a series of operations, it is usually necessary to check only the last hole tapped. Also, a significant saving results from the greatly reduced setup times.

Analysis: In addition to these advantages, another important factor is the minimizing of obsolescence. The numerical control concept, with rapid tape and re-programming changes, makes it possible to adapt the entire line to future model changes, with a variety of engine cylinder blocks, with relative ease and minimum of expense.

CASE STUDY NO. 7

APPLICATION: *Process Switch Boxes on Numerically Controlled Multi-Purpose Machine (Machining Center)*
SAVINGS: *Reduction of 37% in Machining Time, 33% in Tool Costs, Work on Eight Manually Operated Machines Replaced*

Switch boxes in the form of mild-steel castings, shown in Figure 4–11, are processed in 73 separate machining operations in only 22.8 minutes compared with 36.8 minutes before. The work is performed on a Milwaukee-Matic multi-purpose machine or machining center, by Kearney & Trecker Corporation, a type of machine tool first developed by this company and introduced early in 1959 for milling, boring, drilling and a variety of other operations. (Figure 4–12 shows the configuration of a model similar to that used on this application.) General Electric Company provided the numerical control system for the machine.

This machine tool serves as a good example of the results obtained from machines designed from the ground up for the specific purpose of utilizing numerical control for numerous operations on the same machine. This type of machine tool is also referred to as a numerically controlled, automatic machining or production center.

Operations

The 73 machining operations on this part consist of the following separate ones:

Milling	11	Countersinking	11
Boring	1	Reaming	1
Counterboring	1	Back facing	1
Drilling	24	Tapping	12
Counterdrilling	11	Total Operations	73

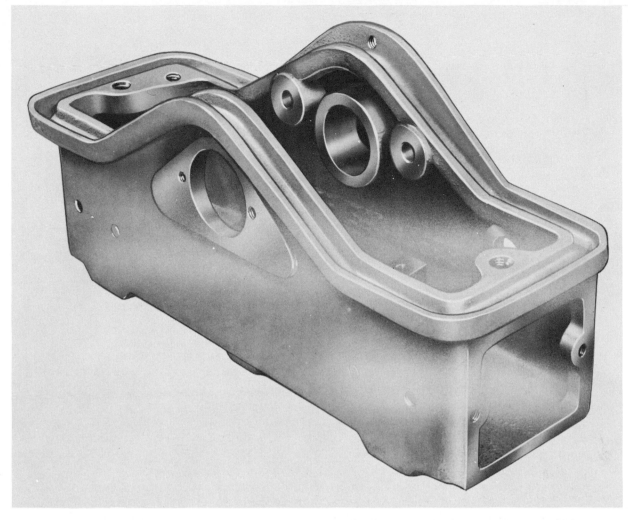

Figures 4–11 & 4–12. At top: Switch box of Case Study No. 7, requiring 73 separate machining operations carried out on a Kearney & Trecker Milwaukee-Matic. (General Electric Company.) At bottom: A general view of the KTNC Milwaukee-Matic with automatic tool changing for 31 different tools, providing a total of 961 different tool conditions. (Kearney & Trecker Corporation.)

The Machine

This Milwaukee-Matic combination milling, drilling and boring machine, capable of numerous additional operations, has an automatic tool changer with 30 tools, and with another tool in the spindle, it provides 31 tools that are available on tape command, for a total of 961 different tool conditions. Tool changes are made in 8 to 9 seconds.

Since the first machine of this type was introduced in 1959 as the KTNC Milwaukee-Matic three-axis tape controlled combination machine, it has been followed by additional models. Its design concept was to bring automation to manufacturers having production runs of small and medium lots in their overall manufacturing program, and to make it possible to perform all required machining operations on a single machine if desired.

Tool selection and changing, positioning, shuttling of workpiece into position via work-supporting pallets, and indexing or rotating the work supporting index table into position as programmed, are all automatic. In addition, spindle speed, feed rate, and auxiliary operations—such as turning the coolant on and off—are also tape controlled. The machine can also cut slopes (angled cuts, usually in a single plane) and arcs, under numerical control.

Programming does not require the use of a computer; punched tape is prepared on a conventional automatic typewriter, such as the Friden Flexowriter (by Friden, Inc.).

Savings: Processing the switch box casting on this NC machine replaces the work of eight manually operated machine tools. A reduction of 37% in the cycle time required to machine the switch box, and about a 33% cut in tool costs, were obtained.

Direct labor cost per part for machining dropped from about $1.51 to about $0.95. (These costs were based on machining lots of 50 parts, with direct labor calculated at $2.50 per hour.) When processing parts suitable for numerical control, it should be possible to write off such a machine in from one and one half to three years. (In a survey conducted by Kearney & Trecker Corporation, to determine the suitability of specific parts for numerically controlled machining, it was found that only about 20% of the parts were considered unsuitable.)

Here are the cost comparisons for the old and new methods:

	CONVENTIONAL OPERATION	NUMERICAL CONTROL OPERATION
Lead time	464 hr.	57 hr.
Setup time	302 min.	0 (with shuttle; see text)
Cycle time	36.3 min.	22.8 min.
Number of machines	8	1
Number of fixtures	2	2
Number of moves	8	0
Tooling cost	$900	$600

Analysis: The numerically controlled machine takes the place of eight other machines, in this application, and requires only one operator. And he does not have to manipulate levers or continually make decisions on the job; he need only keep the machine loaded.

The greatly reduced handling time makes for a more smoothly running shop—no need to move the parts between eight different machines.

Lead time is slashed to about one-eighth of that required to tool up the conventional machines: instead of using special tooling in the form of jigs and fixtures, only two simple work holding fixtures are designed and made. Once the program is laid out and the tape punched, it serves for all repeat runs as well. Although repeat runs are of course carried out also when jigs and fixtures, or/and other special tools, are used for the conventional approach, here the designing of elaborate tools, extensive toolmaking, and considerable tool inspection, are eliminated.

Presetting of cutting tools for the numerical control method, and their replacing (interchanging) in the automatic tool changer magazine, are in this case included in the lead time, as is the installation of the pallets and insertion of the tape. Therefore, no setup time has been shown separately under numerical control in the table. In any event, the setup time on the NC machine is only a fraction of that required for eight conventional machines, and is simpler. Everything falls quickly into place because each step is programmed and tools are set in advance (preset for size) for the automatic tool changer.

CASE STUDY NO. 8

APPLICATION: *Mill Steel Barrel-Cam*
SAVINGS: *Machining Time Reduced from 35 hr. to 6½ hr.*

To mill the cam path in a steel barrel-cam, shown in Figure 4–13, it took 35 hours by the conventional method. Using numerical control this time was cut to 6½ hours. This case study, carried out by General Electric Company, serves to compare NC cam milling with the previous method, which required considerable operator skill.

Figure 4–13. Steel barrel-cam of Case Study No. 8, with groove machined on a Brown & Sharpe Numericam milling machine. (General Electric Company.)

Operation

The Brown & Sharpe Manufacturing Company, using General Electric Mark Series numerical control on its Numericam vertical spindle milling machines, automatically mills a variety of tool jobs including: barrel cams, plate cams, special hole patterns in flat and conical surfaces, and templates.

Approximately 600 points or positions on the cam path (groove) are controlled in milling the barrel cam, to plot the course of the groove.

Savings: Time and labor costs cut from 35 hours to 6½ hours add up to savings of 81%.

Analysis: With the previous method, the operator required a high degree of skill to position the work relative to the cutter at each point, in order to obtain the required cam path.

Using the Numericam machine, from 10 to 16 holes per minute are automatically sunk into the cam surface to form ⅜ in. of the cam's path. Automatic, tape controlled operation eliminates errors in locating and greatly speeds up the entire operation. The operator's functions, after a brief setup, are restricted to loading and unloading the machine. Pressing the start button initiates the cycle each time.

CASE STUDY NO. 9

APPLICATION: *Machine Aircraft Reinforcing Doubler*
SAVINGS: *Drastic Reductions At Every Stage, Lead Time Cut by 80%*

This case involves milling of aircraft structural members at The Boeing Company (Wichita, Kans.).* When Boeing was producing the B-47 aircraft, the lead time—the period from the time the drawing was received by the production planning department, until the first blank was loaded on the machine—was five days for the reinforcing doubler shown in Figure 4–14.

When it was necessary to modernize the B-47, the lead time for the doubler was cut to one day through the use of numerical control. This part is about 14 ft. long.

Appreciable savings in lead time, especially critical in the aerospace industry, were realized by the plant in many additional cases. (In programming for the reinforcing doubler, less than 100 ft. of tape was required.)

Savings: In every area of production, the savings for The Boeing Company were extremely large:

	CONVENTIONAL MACHINING	NUMERICAL CONTROL MACHINING
Lead time	5 days	1 day
Machining time (first part)	25 hr.	1.2 hr.
Machining time (production)	6 hr.	0.5 hr.
Hand finishing	120 min.	10 min.

Analysis: Although the importance of lead time has always been stressed in the aircraft industry, it has the same implications in every other industry—wherever a new manufacturing program is started. Lead time savings have several very tangible results that can be

---

* This aerospace industry case study, also the next one, have been the subject of presentations in a numerical control seminar conducted jointly by Boeing and the American Machine Tool Distributors Association (Washington, D. C.).

translated into dollars and cents; and a great amount of hand finishing was eliminated in this case.

The great reduction in the machining time, however, can also be partially credited to improved cutter design and a re-evaluation of feed rates as used with the NC method.

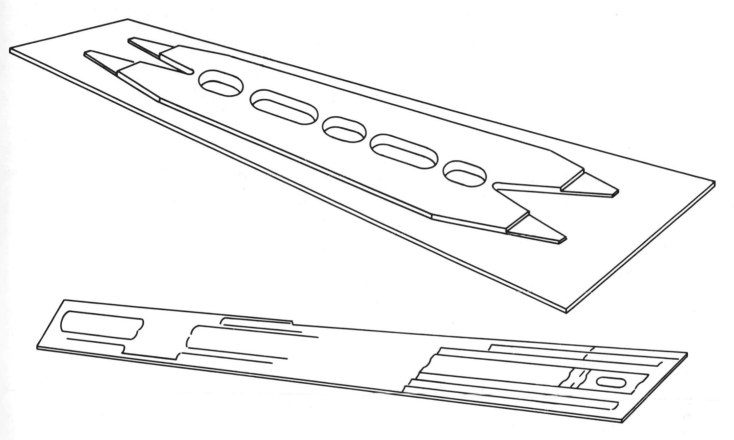

Figures 4–14 & 4–15. At top: Reinforcing doubler for aircraft, Case Study No. 9. At bottom: One of the lower panels for aircraft wing of Case Study No. 9. The Boeing Company (Wichita, Kans.), and American Machine Tool Distributors Association.

CASE STUDY NO. 10

APPLICATION: *Sculpture Inner Surface of Aircraft Wing Panels*
SAVINGS: *Production Machining Time Reduced from 20 Hours to 2½ Hours*

When The Boeing Company (Wichita, Kansas), changed from conventional machining to a numerically controlled skin mill in sculpturing the inner surface of lower panels on the wing of the Boeing-52G, the plant cut production time from 20 hours to 2½ hours. Conventional production was on a template-controlled spar mill.

The panel involved, as in Figure 4–15, is about 76 ft. × 3 ft. The material is aluminum alloy (7178-T6).

Aerospace Production Equipment

Among its large production units, the aircraft or aerospace industry uses large skin and spar milling machines for machining wing skins and other large structural sections. Tracer control has been widely used for these machines in the past. For a number of years, however, the builders of skin mills have made these machines available with numerical control to replace the tracer or copying approach.

When machining members such as the wing panel of Figure 4–15, as much as 75% of the metal may be removed in the form of chips (numerically controlled machining from the solid, instead of forging and then machining, for example).

Savings and Analysis: Production was substantially increased, and additional advantages also accrued as in the previous case study.

CASE STUDY NO. 11

APPLICATION: *Drill Aluminum Sign Bases*
SAVINGS: *62% in Production Time, 79% in Tool Preparation Time*

A maker of precision metal and plastic parts, General Machine & Instrument Company (Caldwell, N. J.), uses a point-to-point, numerically controlled turret drill on a wide variety of parts including missile, aircraft, and electronic assembly components. The machine, a Turr-E-Tape, is made by Brown & Sharpe Manufacturing Company. This case study deals with the completely automatic, tape controlled drilling of four holes in aluminum sign bases.

One of these sign bases, an estimated 10 in. long, is shown at the bottom left of Figure 4–16. The other components in the picture, processed on the same machine, display complex hole patterns. This NC user's output involves operations such as drilling, tapping, boring, reaming and counterboring, in aluminum, stainless steels, and other materials.

Old and New Methods Compared

In the previous method, drilling of the aluminum sign bases was carried out on conventional drills with drilling jigs. In the numerical control method, the four holes are drilled under completely automatic operation.

Only a simple plate holding fixture is now used, and the parts are held for drilling in five stacks of four parts. The comparison follows:

	OLD METHOD, ON CONVENTIONAL DRILLS, WITH JIGS	NEW METHOD, ON NC TURRET DRILL
Tool preparation time	7 hr.	1½ hr.
Machining time	13 hr.	5 hr.
	Drilling jig required	Simple holding fixture used

Savings: Tool preparation time is reduced by nearly 79% and production time by almost 62%. Elimination of the drill jig results in an additional material cost saving of $20.00.

Analysis: Versatility of the NC turret drill used in machining a variety of other parts at General Machine & Instrument provides savings and improved techniques in several directions. For example, the machine may also be operated manually, when machining single pieces. The simple plate holding fixture used for the sign bases was made the manual way.

In general, when only 5 to 10 pieces of the same part are required from this machine, then operations are carried out manually—the automatic cycle of rapid traverse of the

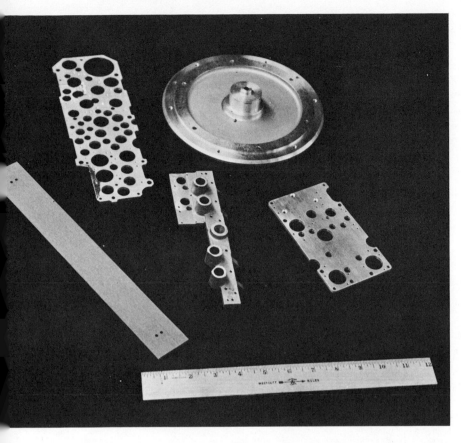

Figure 4–16. Components with complex hole patterns as machined on a Turr-E-Tape drill at General Machine & Instrument Co. Case Study No. 11 part is at bottom left. (Brown & Sharpe Manufacturing company.)

spindle toward the work, power feed control, rapid spindle retraction, automatic indexing, and tapping control, are by-passed. Work positioning, however, is still carried out under tape control, by selecting the required "block" of information on the tape.

Another advantage is that holding fixtures for other components can be made to accommodate several similar parts, eliminating separate drilling jigs for each type of part.

Positioning accuracy of the table is stated as ± 0.001 in. per foot; the machine operates to within ± 0.0005 in., according to this user. Holes up to 1¼ in. diameter have been drilled in aluminum. Use of the NC positioning table makes for rapid changeovers from one job to the next.

CASE STUDY NO. 12

This study is an overall report of a numerical control installation in one plant, the Woodward Governor Company (Rockford, Ill.).

The company took delivery of a Cleereman Spindlemaster, a vertical-spindle machine with 30-station automatic tool changer, for drilling, milling, tapping, boring and a variety of additional operations. The machine's builder is Cleereman Machine Tool Corporation.

The first few weeks were spent installing the machine, trouble shooting, running sample parts and trying out tooling, Woodward Governor reported. Within the next 15 months, the latter had about 200 parts programmed and in production at different times. The lot sizes ran from as few as 5 pieces to as many as 150, with most orders totalling 25 to 50 pieces of the same type.

Tools and Tool Savings

The company has held fixturing for the machine to a minimum. Several "universal" fixtures have been designed and made so that they can be used for a number of different parts with only an accompanying change of locating pins and clamping when changing from one type of part to another. The other fixtures are simple holding plates. In contrast to the making of drill jigs and fixtures, no bushings or expensive grinding operations are necessary.

Although Woodward Governor has not tabulated its exact savings in fixturing, it estimates them to be worth $7,000 during the first year. The company considers this saving as being low, because of the fact that fixtures were already on hand for many of the parts. These fixtures were subsequently stripped of details that were no longer required for locating or alignment and now are used as simple holding fixtures.

Variety of Production Operations

A wide range of machining operations is carried out, from the simple drilling of numerous holes in some parts to combinations of drilling, boring, milling and tapping in more complicated components.

The company's range of tapping runs from sizes of No. 4-40 (0.112 in. diam., 40 threads per in.) to 1.625-16 taps (the latter $1\frac{5}{8}$ in., 16 threads per in.), and the plant reported that no trouble had been encountered. This tapping has been in aluminum and cast iron for the latter large-size taps; tapping in steel has also been carried out, but not with the very small or very large taps.

Substantial Savings

According to the company, its savings in machining over conventional methods are about 40%, and they range from 25% on some parts to 80% on others. Savings of this magnitude are the result of combining several operations of drilling and milling into one operation on the same machine.

The automatic tool changer provides considerable versatility, and coupled with numerical positioning of the work, it obviates setting up and operating several machines. In addition, moving of parts to different machines or departments is eliminated.

Organizing for Numerical Control

Machine utilization time for this installation has been excellent. "Down time has been held to 5% by the education of our electricians and machine repairmen. They have had training from both control and machine manufacturers. The down time is divided almost equally between electrical and mechanical trouble," reported Woodward Governor Company.

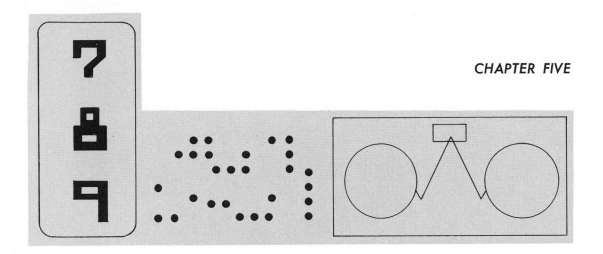

CHAPTER FIVE

APPLICATIONS WHERE
NUMERICAL CONTROL PAYS OFF

SPECIFIC EXAMPLES OF SAVINGS AND THE ADVANTAGES DERIVED FROM NUMERICAL CONTROL APPLICATIONS WERE GIVEN IN THE CASE STUDIES OF CHAPTER 4. SHORT TO MEDIUM RUNS—EVEN OF SINGLE PIECES IN SOME CASES—RATHER THAN HIGH VOLUME PRODUCTION, USUALLY FORM THE MOST PROFITABLE BASIS FOR APPLYING NUMERICAL CONTROL. HOWEVER, NUMERICAL CONTROL IS ALSO MOVING INTO THE HIGHER-VOLUME AREA IN SOME APPLICATIONS.

THE PRODUCTS OF NC MANUFACTURING RANGE FROM CONSUMER ITEMS SUCH AS ELECTRIC AND ELECTRONIC APPLIANCES TO CAPITAL EQUIPMENT IN THE HEAVY MACHINERY CLASS, SUCH AS TURBINES, JET LINERS, AND GIANT MACHINE TOOLS.

Manufacturing of General Machinery

MACHINERY MANUFACTURING OR BUILDING IN GENERAL, OF LIGHT TO HEAVY MACHINES, EMBRACES

63

a great many industries. In the sections following, machinery such as electric and power plant machinery, machine tools, railway equipment, and some other classes, will be treated under separate headings.

General machinery involves both standard and custom-built units. An almost unlimited variety of parts, and many variations of each general type of part, are produced with numerical control by machinery building plants. These are in the metals, metal products, and related metalworking industries, although the materials used are not confined to metals. Representative examples of machinery parts produced with numerical control are:

Machine housings	Machine frames	Miscellaneous supports, brackets, etc.
Gear cases	Drive cases	Other structural members
Speed reducer housings	Covers	
Machine bases	Other enclosures	

POINT-TO-POINT

The above are applications involving accurate but fast and economical hole location and spacing (point-to-point numerical control) for such operations as drilling, boring, reaming, and tapping of holes, also straight-line milling or similar machining of plane or other surfaces in the same setup, if rate control is included.

Most of these parts start as castings, some as weldments, and others can be machined "from the solid." In addition, plate and sheet work for other types of covers, enclosures, panels and similar parts, makes use of numerically controlled punch presses or fabricating machines.

POINT-TO-POINT WITH RATE CONTROL

Aside from straight-cut milling jobs done on NC drilling machines, machining centers, and other machines having positioning control plus feed rate control, there are many other uses for systems with rate or straight-cut control. Stepped shafts and many other multi-diameter parts in wide variety are applications for feed-rate controlled point-to-point or positioning systems on lathes and other turning and boring machines. This control over length and diameter of cuts, together with tape control over speed and feed changes, turret indexing, and the like, results in profitable production in operations such as turning, boring, and facing.

CONTOUR OR CONTINUOUS-PATH

Representative examples requiring contouring or continuous-path control are:

PARTS FOR TURNING, BORING, AND RELATED OPERATIONS	PARTS FOR MILLING OPERATIONS (CHIEFLY)
Complex contoured or profiled shafts	Parts requiring complex contour milling operations
Stepped and contoured shafts or machine spindles	Components requiring pocket and special cavity milling
Other contoured parts	Castings or forgings difficult to tool by conventional means
Spherical shapes	
Hemispherical shapes	Other machine parts requiring complicated contour milling or combined machining operations
Covers, supports, etc.	
Special gear blanks and sleeves	Pump vanes, contoured pump parts, and similar elements
Other contoured, operational elements	
Other static, contoured parts	Cam follower grooves
Housings	Cams
Special bearing housings	Complex housings
Numerous other parts	Intricate parts machined from the solid

HEAVY MACHINERY

The building of heavy machinery provides numerical control applications similar to the above, except that the parts are larger and heavier. The forms of materials used are castings, forgings, billets and heavy bar stock, plate, and weldments (fabricated from plate and other structural sections). (See also sections following on machine tools and other machinery, electric and power plant machinery, shipyard output, and the like.)

Electric and Electronic Industry Products

The applications here again are usually not to high-volume production but to components required in short runs, or which would otherwise incur prohibitive tooling costs.

MACHINING APPLICATIONS

Parts for machining operations such as drilling, tapping, boring and milling include housings and enclosures for various types of electrical equipment: special motor bases, switch boxes, frames, and the like. Computer components in the electronics field form a special category.

Electric motor couplings, switchgear components, machined parts for electric power lines, are some additional applications. Also: printed circuit board drilling, particularly for specialty electric and electronic appliances or equipment; most of this is for point-to-point control.

PUNCH PRESS WORK

Sheet metal parts requiring varied hole patterns in short runs of about 10 to 100 pieces, depending on type of part, where special high-volume tooling costs are not justified, provide payoff applications in electric and electronic products. In some cases, higher runs, perhaps up to 500 parts or even more, can be profitable when using numerical control. Typical parts are:

Panels	Instrument chassis (e.g., chassis for	Enclosures for: electronic switch gear, electronic
Frames	electronic testing instruments)	apparatus, communications equipment
Covers	Control cabinet sections	Special instrument panels
	Cabinet doors	Special blanked or cut-out parts for structural
		subassemblies

NUMERICALLY CONTROLLED PUNCHING EQUIPMENT USED

The equipment used here can be "fabricating centers" for punching, notching and allied operations, numerically controlled turret-type punch presses, or other machines. Figure 5–1 shows examples of work, such as electric and electronic panels and chassis, produced on machines by Wales Strippit Company (see Figure 5–2). Punch presses of the turret type, for example, performing similar operations, are made by the Wiedemann Division, The Warner & Swasey Company.

Machine Tools and Other Production Machinery

Good numerical control applications here are housings, enclosures, frames and covers of many types requiring precision locating, spacing and boring of holes. Others are a variety of parts requiring a broad range of milling operations, also step-shaft and contour-shaft turn-

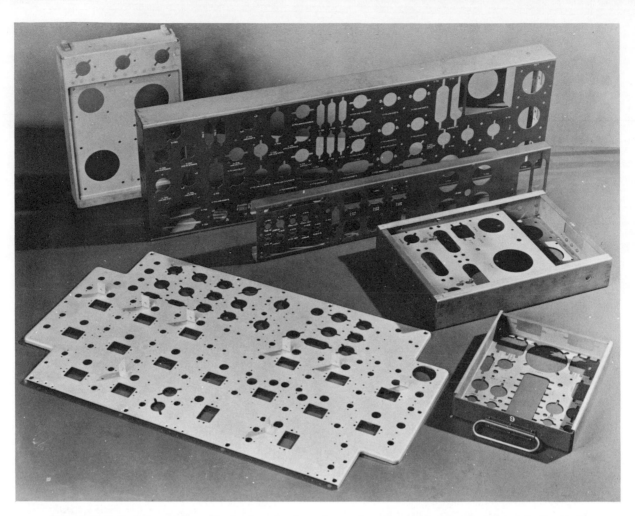

Figures 5-1 & 5-2. At top: Typical examples of punch press work for electric and electronic products. (Wales Strippit Company.) At bottom: NC "fabricating center" for work as in Fig.5-1. (Wales Strippit Company.)

ing and related operations. The parts or members are for machine tools ranging from standard light to heavy duty machine tools, from conventional types to special-purpose and transfer machines, and for "elephant" or giant machine tools. The machines include conventional and NC types. Practically all types of metal cutting operations are involved here (see also Tables 1 and 2). Additional applications are machine tool accessories such as coolant pump bodies and similar products, parts for machine control systems, hydraulic elements, and other parts.

Electric and Power Plant Machinery

Electrical equipment, and machinery for electric power generation, employ components suited to numerical control manufacture basically similar to those for general machinery manufacturing and heavy machinery building, with the addition of others.

Numerical control is used in varying degrees to produce equipment for thermal, hydro-electric, as well as nuclear reactor power plants. Representative parts and products are:

Turbine blades (turbine buckets)
Big housings, gear cases
Generator rotors
Special machine bases
Rotor shafts for turbines
Stepped and contoured shafts for rotating machinery

Feed-water heater parts
Heat exchanger parts (gun drilling of tube sheets, etc.)
Gas turbines
Steam turbine-generators
Other parts for electric machinery of all types as suited to NC processing

Engines, Automotive Equipment for Construction Industry

Manufacturing diesel engine cylinder blocks for earthmoving machinery on a transfer line, almost wholly tape controlled, was described in Chapter 4. Other parts of various types of construction machinery call for numerically controlled applications, similar to those for general machinery manufacturing or heavy machinery building as already described.

Tooling for Production

Machining the specialized tools required for high-volume production, as an important area of numerical control applications, could well be near the top of this list. Numerical control expedites and makes possible the production of tooling formerly almost impossible to turn out due to its complexity, and in other cases, it makes such tooling more economical to produce when compared with conventional methods. Examples of tools are:

Complicated templates for tracer machining
Intricate masters or models of three-dimensional type
Other complex templates
Forging dies (e.g., for automotive industry)
Other press tools, e.g., punch holders, punches, dies
Jigs
Fixtures
Other special tooling
Drilling, punching, or punch-locating templates
Cams

Laying out, center-punching or spot drilling of sheet metal and similar parts for subsequent hole punching, etc.
Punch holders for steel rule dies
Precision template scribing for bandsawing and subsequent contour grinding
Complex plastic or glass molds
Big die sets
Other intricate tooling

Templates and masters requiring special profiles or shapes are contouring applications, while hole locating as in jigs and related tooling calls for point-to-point numerical control.

AEROSPACE INDUSTRY TOOLING

Important applications here are: intricate templates, three-dimensional masters, models, aircraft templates, profile bars, honeycomb dies (cavities), follower cams or templates for skin mills, shearing dies, and profile mill fixtures. Additional tool applications are similar to or overlap with the examples of the preceding list.

Automotive and Related Industries

Numerical control has not made any great inroads in the direct production of passenger cars and trucks, which involves high-volume output that is achieved through conventional automation—transfer lines and special-purpose machines. The NC transfer line principle, however, as already described, can be applied in additional automotive-type industries where quantities are not in the high-volume class.

Other parts for various related industries include engine flywheels, housings, bases, and the like, generally where small lots are needed.

Diesel Locomotive Engines, Railroad Transportation Equipment

Production of diesel locomotive engines was increased about 20% at a plant of The Cooper-Bessemer Corporation (Grove City, Penna.), through acquisition of a 5 in. numerically controlled floor-type horizontal boring, drilling and milling machine (a product of The Cincinnati Gilbert Machine Tool Company).

Even greater time savings were obtained on individual operations: on one engine base alone, the company was able to scrap six jigs costing up to $6,000 each, replacing them with numerically controlled point-to-point operations. In addition, an acre of plant space formerly devoted to jig storage was made available. Cincinnati Gilbert reported operation of three shifts a day and six days a week for this machine, which was joined since by others of the same kind, purchased by Cooper-Bessemer.

Shipyard Output

Applications of numerical control in shipyards covers ships' power plant and propulsion machinery as well as platework and various structural members in a wide range of operations. In addition, there is much ancillary equipment. Representative jobs include make-up shafts for cargo passenger ships and tube sheet production.

Figure 5–3 shows an 8 ft. diameter tube sheet with 1,000 holes drilled in it under positioning control, at Bethlehem Steel Company (Burns Harbor, Ind. plant). Bethlehem Steel is a large user of numerical control.

Structural Steel and Plate Fabrications

Numerical control is used in structural steel fabricating shops in the fabrication of steel beams, columns, and other structural sections. Point-to-point control is used to locate beams and other structural sections for operations such as drilling, reaming, punching or piercing. Other products are various plate fabrications produced by cutting plate and welding sections into required assemblies or subassemblies.

The final products for the prefabricated components or assemblies are bridges, build-

Figure 5–3. This 8 ft. diam. tube sheet has 1,000 holes drilled in it under numerical control. (Bethlehem Steel Company.)

ings, other structures, and in some cases, heavy machine frames or other structural machine sections.

Steel Mill Rolls

Rolls for steel rolling mills require special contours to compensate for rolling stresses, and are often contour ground on numerically controlled machines, both in original manufacture and in maintenance.

In addition to the use of cylindrical grinders for this work, there are numerous other applications for numerical control for building heavy machinery for steel mill and allied operations.

Aerospace Industry Output

Embracing aircraft of various types, space exploration craft and its equipment, as well as missile manufacture, the aerospace industry continues as a large user of numerically controlled equipment. In addition to tooling, already given, aerospace industry applications and products, predominantly reflecting contouring uses, feature great variety. Among examples are wing skins (milled from the solid), various integral subassemblies replacing sheet-metal fabrications, compressor casings for jet engines, compressor stator and rotor blades, missile parts, rockets, rocket engine parts, and many others.

Products Requiring Tube and Pipe Bending

Formed or specially bent tubing components are used extensively in aircraft and missile work, and may be economically produced with numerically controlled tube bending or forming machines. Also, in the automotive replacement parts market, for example, tailpipes are required in a great variety of configurations. To reduce inventories, tape-controlled bending, which can be put into action on short notice, can be resorted to. Extensive piping systems of various processing industries can also make use of this method.

Products of Other Industries

Numerous additional industries, which cannot all be listed here, have one or more products for which parts may be more profitably manufactured under numerical control. The parts selected for NC processing, depending on the individual industry, are similar to one or more of the parts and the products already given in this chapter.

Custom machine shops, tool shops, and press work shops apply numerical control to good advantage on short to medium runs, competing with conventional methods.

(See Table 1 for a list of basic numerical control operations, and Table 2 for numerically controlled machines. Although numerical control could be applied in one way or another to practically any machine tool or production unit, not all such machines can be listed in the latter table.)

Measuring and Inspection Machines, Drafting Machines

Inspection of hole locations is speeded up considerably by the use of coordinate measuring or inspection machines. These are closely related to numerical control systems, since they essentially use the measuring (feedback) portion of an NC system. They provide precision measurements at hole locations according to X and Y coordinates (also to a Z coordinate, if a three-axis measuring system is employed). Usually, a probe is moved manually from one hole to the next. The actual coordinates are then automatically displayed at the same time, in digital form. This digital readout can be augmented by an automatic printout, which provides a permanent record of each job or component.

Additional types of measuring machines have a microscope or other means for checking various dimensions, together with, in effect, numerical control feedback, plus digital readout of actual dimensions.

More advanced, tape controlled, multi-axis machines are employed for measuring and recording complex contours.

Automatic, numerically controlled drafting machines, although not occurring as frequently as NC machine tools, have several important uses.

Numerical control tape that has been prepared by computer routines for complex machining or other operations can be proved or verified on such drafting machines. This saves running off a test part on a large machine tool. An NC drafting machine may also be capable of converting mathematical formulae into drawings of parts or tools such as templates—it can produce exact scale drawings.

Other and Newer NC Machines and Applications

Numerically controlled contour flame cutting machines as well as fusion welders have been developed, and further work is continuing.

Additional or projected numerical control applications and developments include:

- automatic wiring machines
- card or tape operated rolling mills
- research for generating high-precision gear teeth without use of other gears
- simulation of service conditions in testing parts and materials
- the use of positioning control for broaching operations
- further development of filament winding (fiber glass strands for missile components, etc.)
- the developing use of various "robots" for tool or part handling, and the like
- digital plotting machines
- research on ultra-fine boring, using the laser principle
- remote controlling of machines operating in the vicinity of explosives or radioactivity, and remote contour machining of highly explosive solid propellants
- lofting of ships' hulls
- data logging or gathering of operational data
- applications in industries other than metalworking; for example, in printing, where tape, with the aid of computers, has advanced beyond the Teletypesetting stage
- use of numerical control for plant production control, as well as in further developments

TABLE 1

OPERATIONS FOR NUMERICAL CONTROL

METAL CUTTING OR MACHINING—MOST CHIP-REMOVAL PROCESSES, SUCH AS:	POSITIONING OR POINT-TO-POINT CONTROL	CONTOURING OR CONTINUOUS-PATH CONTROL	METAL CUTTING OR MACHINING—CONTINUED	POSITIONING OR POINT-TO-POINT CONTROL	CONTOURING OR CONTINUOUS-PATH CONTROL
Drilling	x		Milling	x	x
Tapping	x		Contour, profile milling		x
Boring	x	x	Pocket milling	x	x
Reaming	x		Die sinking and		
Counterboring	x		multi-dimensional		
Countersinking	x		milling		x
Spot facing	x		Cam milling		x
Spot drilling	x		Thread cutting		x
Center drilling	x		Thread milling		x
Turning	x	x	Jig boring	x	
Contour turning		x	Jig grinding	x	
Step (multi-diameter)			Profile grinding		x
turning	x	x	Cylindrical and other		
Step boring	x	x	contour grinding		x
Contour boring		x	Step (multi-diameter)		
Facing, stepfacing	x	x	grinding	x	x
Contour facing		x	Roll grinding		x

Continued—Table 1

Operations for Numerical Control

METAL CUTTING OR MACHINING— CONTINUED	POSITIONING OR POINT- TO-POINT CONTROL	CONTOURING OR CONTINUOUS- PATH CONTROL
Template grinding		x
Turbine or compressor blade grinding		x
Cam grinding		x
Additional specialized machining operations	x	x
PUNCHING AND METAL FORMING— cutting by non-chip removing processes, press-working		
Hole piercing	x	
Notching	x	
Blanking or cutting-out	x	
Nibbling, or cutting-out with series of holes, etc.	x	
Forming	x	
Other punching and forming operations	x	
Tube bending	x	
Riveting	x	
MEASURING AND INSPECTION		
Contour and general measuring operations		x
Coordinate measuring (e.g., manual input)	x	

MEASURING AND INSPECTION— CONTINUED	POSITIONING OR POINT- TO-POINT CONTROL	CONTOURING OR CONTINUOUS- PATH CONTROL
Other precision inspection operations	x	x
Precision layout operations	x	
NEWER OPERATIONS		
Drafting machine operations	x	x
Welding	x	x
Flame cutting		x
Forging	x	
Assembling, especially combined welding and assembly	x	x
Handling and transferring by robot	x	x
Heat treating	x	
Plating	x	
Filament winding (see also text)	x	x
Additional operations: any others where positioning, complex motions, sequencing and cycling of processes must be controlled	—	—

(Please note: See also footnotes with Table 2)

TABLE 2

MACHINES FOR NUMERICAL CONTROL

DRILLING MACHINES —FOR DRILLING, BORING, REAMING, TAPPING, ETC.	POSITIONING OR POINT-TO-POINT CONTROL	CONTOURING OR CONTINUOUS-PATH CONTROL
Vertical or upright drills, general	x	
Turret drills	x	
Layout drills	x	
Radial drills	x	
Special production drilling machines	x	
Printed circuit board drilling machines	x	
Other types	x	
MILLING MACHINES		
Vertical spindle, knee or other type	x	x
Die sinking and profile milling machines		x
Bridge or rail type milling machines		x
Skin and spar milling machines		x
Profile mills		x
Contour milling machines		x
Special aerospace industry milling machines		x
Cam milling machines		x
Other types	x	x
NC MACHINING OR PRODUCTION CENTERS		
Manual tool changing types	x	x
Automatic tool changing types	x	x
TURNING MACHINES —LATHES AND OTHER		
NC engine lathes	x	x
NC production lathes	x	x
Turret lathes	x	x
Vertical turret lathes (see also vertical boring and turning mills, below)	x	x
Other and special lathes	x	x

BORING MACHINES, INCLUDING JIG BORERS	POSITIONING OR POINT-TO-POINT CONTROL	CONTOURING OR CONTINUOUS-PATH CONTROL
Horizontal boring, drilling and milling machines (horizontal boring mills)	x	x
Vertical spindle jig borers	x	
Horizontal jig borers	x	
Vertical boring and turning mills (see also vertical turret lathes, above)	x	x
Other precision boring machines	x	x
PRECISION GRINDING MACHINES		
Cylindrical grinders	x	
Roll grinders		x
Contour grinding machines		x
Jig grinders	x	
Cam grinding machines		x
Template grinding machines		x
Special airfoil (turbine, compressor blades) grinding machines		x
Other precision grinding machines	x	x
PUNCHING, FORMING AND BENDING MACHINES		
Punching and related-operation machines	x	
Turret punch presses	x	
Combination punching or fabricating machines (centers)	x	
Other fabricating machines	x	
Tube and pipe bending machines	x	
Riveting machines	x	

Continued—Table 2

Machines for Numerical Control

MEASURING AND INSPECTION MACHINES	POSITIONING OR POINT-TO-POINT CONTROL	CONTOURING OR CONTINUOUS-PATH CONTROL	NEWER TYPES OF NC MACHINES—CONTINUED	POSITIONING OR POINT-TO-POINT CONTROL	CONTOURING OR CONTINUOUS-PATH CONTROL
Contour and general-purpose measuring machine	x	x	Filament winding machines	x	x
Coordinate measuring, inspection machines	x		Forging machines	x	
Other inspection and layout machines	x	x	Robot transferring and handling machines	x	x
NEWER TYPES OF NC MACHINES			Processing or production lines with numerical control over sequence of operation, positioning, or intricate motions	—	—
Drafting and tape verification machines	x	x			
Welding machines	x	x			
Contour flame cutting machines		x			
Combined assembling and welding machines	x	x			

Please Note:

1. Straight-line milling and similar operations can be performed with various point-to-point systems using rate control for individual machine motions; some other applications and exceptions are possible. Step turning, step grinding, and related operations are on a similar basis.

2. Universal or combination systems combine both positioning and contouring control.

3. NC grinding operations, such as cylindrical grinding, are not as prevalent as the other chip-removal processes.

4. The operations listed are not restricted to metals, but can include plastics, other nonmetallics and materials.

5. Coordinate inspection machines usually combine manual actuation with automatic measuring and visual digital display.

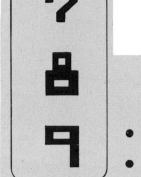
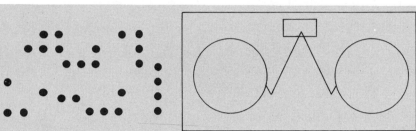

CHAPTER SIX

PINPOINTING ADDITIONAL, POTENTIAL APPLICATIONS—A SUMMARY

TO "PINPOINT" POTENTIAL NUMERICAL CONTROL APPLICATIONS—ASIDE FROM THE USES DESCRIBED IN THE THE PRECEDING PAGES—CAN BE DONE PROPERLY ONLY BY EXAMINING THE OPERATIONS AND PRODUCTS OF A PARTICULAR PLANT. HOWEVER, SUGGESTIONS CAN BE GIVEN TO ASSIST IN THIS PROCESS.

Examining Specific Production Operations

ANALYZING ROUTINE TECHNIQUES

TO SEARCH OUT ADDITIONAL, POTENTIAL APPLICATIONS, IT IS WELL TO EXAMINE THE ROUTINE TECHNIQUES BEING USED—THE OLD-ESTABLISHED PROCEDURES FOR A PRODUCTION OPERATION OR A SERIES OF OPERATIONS.

IF THE PLANT HAS NOT CHANGED OR IMPROVED A ROUTINE FOR A NUMBER OF YEARS, THIS MAY BE A GOOD POINT TO START, AS THE APPROACH MAY be obsolete. Comparing each step with what numerical control would do in its place, may yield more results than may at first be apparent.

When replacing any operations with numerically controlled ones, the latest applicable cutter and tool designs, and procedures, should be included at the same time. Cutting speeds, feeds, and other operating conditions, should be re-examined as well.

TOOL AND WORKPIECE CHANGING

An example of frequent manual tool changing is in the machining of small lots in milling machine production when a series of operations must all be performed in one work setting. Interchanging arbor-mounted cutters, or even using quick-change holders, may be improved upon considerably with numerical control and automatic tool changes.

There are other parallel examples in both metal cutting and metal forming. The same applies when the workpiece must be moved from one machine to another for the various operations.

In drilling and related work, in small and medium lots, if a series of operations, such as drilling, boring, reaming, etc., must be carried out at the same hole or work positions, this can be speeded up with numerical control. It greatly shortens the time for the repeated work positioning.

OPERATIONS TO PRECISION TOLERANCES

In machining operations, if tolerances are in the order of ± 0.001 or less, the use of numerical control may be indicated.

MANUAL INDEXING ON TURRET LATHES

How much does it cost a plant for manual indexing of the hexagon and square turrets on turret lathes? Operator fatigue costs money and is inadvisable, and in piecework, it causes dissatisfaction. If conventional automatic machines for high volume are not justified, then numerical control should be investigated.

STRAIGHT-LINE MILLING

Medium and light duty milling can be economically performed, at the same work settings, on medium-capacity point-to-point drills with straight-cut or feed-rate control. (Such milling cuts can include slots, pockets, and the like.)

TAPPING OPERATIONS

Tapping of threads is involved in a great majority of machine components. Tapping is frequently the *last* operation on a part that may already represent considerable precision machining time and labor cost. When taps break or threads are stripped, it is not the value of the taps that generally matters—but that of the part. High scrap rates and rework costs can result from tapping operations.

Numerically controlled tapping is often preferable. The operation is under better control at all times; it is automatic, and the operator can observe the operation closely. As the workpiece remains clamped in the same setting, the holding problem is also taken care of.

Tapping many small holes on the larger NC machines, however, may not be economical —it can instead be made a secondary operation on separate, but well-chosen equipment. This may be placed alongside the NC machine, and attended by the same operator.

NON-UNIFORM CUTTING SPEEDS

When there are big variations in the diameters of a workpiece, as happens in many turning and boring operations, especially on continuous cuts, it is difficult or impossible to keep the peripheral or cutting speed uniform. Numerical control can be used to program uniform cutting speeds, if the machine drive will accommodate this procedure.

Savings of 35 to 50% can be obtained with constant cutting speeds, as the machining process is then utilized to optimum advantage. Better surface finishes result at the same time, and dimensional control is improved.

METAL FORMING, PUNCHING OPERATIONS

Looking into these operations, similarly to machining, can bring equivalent results. Although constant cutting speed, for example, is not applicable in the same sense here as in machining, many of the other factors are.

Fast tool changing by rotary turret or other means, and rapid, automatic work positioning, can be achieved with numerical control.

ROTARY APPLICATIONS

Although power driven and automatically indexed rotary tables of conventional types are available—for milling, drilling, or other operations—numerically controlled rotary positioning should be considered also.

INSPECTION REQUIREMENTS

If many of the parts to be made require 100% inspection, then numerically controlled production can reduce this inspection considerably. Repetitive positioning accuracy and improved uniformity of parts reduce inspection requirements.

HIGH LABOR REQUIREMENTS

If a part has particularly high labor costs or labor content, the use of NC manufacturing instead of conventional production, is frequently the more economical.

In addition, when fully automatic numerical control is utilized, it alleviates skilled-labor shortages.

DESIGN CHANGES

When design changes for a part or product are frequent, and when lead time must be short, then NC manufacturing is often the most economical and efficient method. In addition, if the parts are complex, this is another reason for considering or changing to numerical control.

General Plant Improvement

Where general plant improvements or better work flow may be called for, numerically controlled equipment can lead in a number of ways.

REDUCING MANUAL HANDLING

When much manual manipulation or handling is performed, either at or between machines, the use of numerical control may be indicated.

PARTS HANDLING AT MACHINES

Although the factor of reduced parts handling parallels the previous suggestion, it is well to stress again the integration possible with multi-operation, numerically controlled machines.

CONGESTED PLANT AREAS

If production areas are congested with machines or parts and materials flow, numerically controlled installations may solve the problem.

INVENTORY PRACTICE

If inventories are a problem—continually too high or too low—it may be solved by applying the shorter lead times and faster setup times that feature tape-controlled machines.

OLDER OR OBSOLESCENT INSTALLATIONS

This suggestion, while obvious, emphasizes the fact that the majority of machine tools in use are usually over 10 years old, and obsolescence can be a pervading condition. Numerically controlled machines have an important role to play in the replacement area. Conducting on-the-job studies of all doubtful machines is good practice at any time.

TABLE 3

REPRESENTATIVE AREAS OF ADDITIONAL, POTENTIAL APPLICATIONS

OPERATIONAL FACTORS OR AREAS	GENERAL PLANT OR COMPANY FACTORS
Older or static operations and techniques	Excessive manual handling on or near machines
Tool changing with multiplicity of tools	Excessive work movement between machines
Precision work or tool positioning taking up valuable jig bore¹ time, etc.	Congested plant areas
Work requiring precision tolerances	Inventory problems, delivery problems or delays
Excessive manual indexing of tool turrets	Older or obsolescent machines
Work requiring straight-cut milling combined with drilling and related operations	Products unchanged for a long time
Tapping operations and rework	Products or parts with imminent design changes, or with frequent changes in design
Operations with non-uniform cutting speeds	Projected or new products
Punching and forming (piercing, notching, forming, bending)	Newer or combined concepts, e.g., NC transfer lines
Rotary applications	(Review of all NC advantages—operational and management factors—and matching with specific plant or company requirements)
Manufacturing operations requiring 100% inspection	
High labor content of specific parts or products	

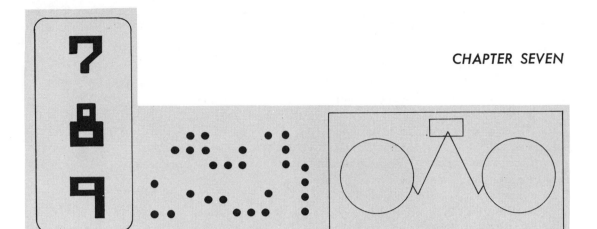

CHAPTER SEVEN

DEFINING SUITABLE LIMITS
FOR NUMERICAL CONTROL

THE MANAGEMENT EXECUTIVE WHO IS ASSESSING NUMERICALLY CONTROLLED PRODUCTION, AND THE MANUFACTURING ENGINEER WHO IS IN CHARGE OF PRODUCTION PLANNING, MUST ALWAYS BE CONCERNED WITH DEFINING LIMITS FOR THE APPLICATION OF NUMERICAL CONTROL, AND FOR PRODUCTION QUANTITIES.

ALTHOUGH THE PROCESS OF ESTABLISHING PRACTICAL LIMITS FOR NUMERICAL CONTROL APPLICATION—WHERE TO START AND WHERE TO STOP—AGAIN HINGES LARGELY ON INDIVIDUAL CONDITIONS, SOME GENERAL GUIDES CAN BE GIVEN. THEY DEPEND ON BASIC FACTORS, INCLUDING: INVENTORY, COMPARISONS OF PRODUCTION RUNS AMONG CONVENTIONAL AND NUMERICALLY CONTROLLED METHODS, ECONOMIC LOT SIZES, AND OTHER CONDITIONS.

79

Basic Factors

To establish or define limits for numerical control, after the application areas have been determined, the following basic factors should be considered:

Limits of capital investment in the NC machine or machinery

Value of parts and machine output

Inventory (and relation to economic lot sizes)

Comparison of numerically controlled and conventional production runs or quantities

Economic lot sizes

Other or special conditions.

Defining the limits of investment and justifying numerical control will be discussed in Chapters 8 and 9. The others are dealt with here.

Value of Parts and of Machine Output

The selling value of the part as well as of the quantity produced must be considered in connection with the machine hour rate, as in all production planning. A product of extremely low value may be better produced by an entirely different manufacturing technique for which numerical control may not yet be available.

Since the numerically controlled machine may represent an appreciably greater investment than the comparable conventional one, the machine hour rate may have to be set at a higher level. This in itself should not mean higher costs per part, but the contrary, as shown in the case studies covered in Chapter 4.

SETTING MACHINE HOUR RATE

In setting the machine hour rate—which is, briefly, the total overhead for the machine divided by the machine hours—none of the many separate factors comprising the total machine hour rate should be overlooked.

All conditions entering into the overhead rate, labor rate, depreciation rate, and the like, must be considered. Each of these must be calculated on an individual basis to suit the application involved.

SOME NON-PROFITABLE OPERATIONS

Some representative examples of operations that may be better performed with the properly selected conventional methods, are:

1. Applications where relatively cheap drill jigs and machines of limited accuracy are sufficient will not likely prove profitable for the introduction of numerical control. Parts with relatively large positioning tolerances are in the same category.

2. Where semi-special, economical and adjustable tooling is freely available, its use may be preferable. An adjustable multi-spindle or cluster drill attachment and jig may do the job more cheaply, especially if tolerances are wide.

3. On higher volume production, except where parts and production runs are suitable for numerical control (for instance, with wide use of fast tool changers on machining centers, and with numerically controlled transfer lines), conventional methods may be more economical.

Comparison: Conventional vs. NC Inventory

Because quantities as small as one or two pieces can often be economically produced with numerical control, inventory can be much smaller than with conventional production. As a result, the most economical lot sizes for machining or other processing can be considerably smaller than by conventional methods.

The chart of Figure 7–1, by The Cincinnati Milling Machine Company, compares standard and numerically controlled machining in their effects on inventory. Notable reductions in the minimum balance A, the average inventory B, and the lot size C, or number of parts per run, are achieved when numerical control is introduced.

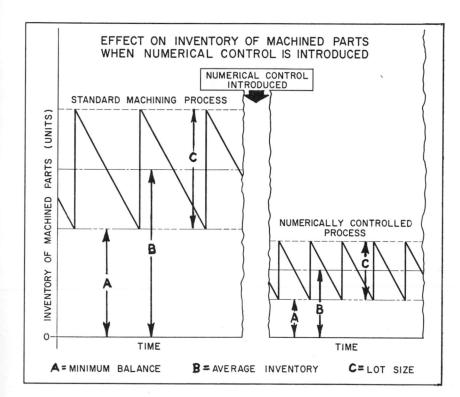

Figure 7–1. Effects on inventory, including lot size, when introducing numerical control. (The Cincinnati Milling Machine Co.)

Comparisons of Numerically Controlled and Conventional Production Runs

In comparing the quantities of production runs—from small quantities to high-volume production—and in determining lot sizes for manufacturing, two main points should be kept in mind:

1. Hourly outputs of different machines cannot be compared directly—for example, a relatively short run for a multi-spindle bar automatic may be a long run for a conventional turret lathe, both being able to do the work.

2. Economic lot sizes (see sections following) or the number of parts per run, must

also be based—aside from inventory considerations—on the total or annual quantity required. The latter may represent the number of pieces required in a whole year or in several years. This quantity determines tooling and programming costs.

TOOLING, PLANNING AND PROGRAMMING COSTS
BASED ON ANNUAL OR TOTAL REQUIREMENT

The preceding point regarding the total or *annual* requirement applies because the costs of the extra tooling—whether simple fixtures for numerical control or more complex jigs, fixtures and other tools for conventional machining—and the production planning or the NC programming as a whole, must be based on the whole or annual quantity to be produced. In some cases, this quantity will be a plant's or customer's total order, yet it may be produced in several lots instead of in a single run.

In some cases, the entire quantity may be a single run, as noted; in others, up to 5, 10, or more runs or lots may be scheduled to produce a required quantity in a year. The separate lots may represent repeat runs for a standard product, as in repetitive manufacturing.

Tooling costs and any comparisons of numerical control and conventional methods must, therefore, be based on the entire quantity required, not on the individual run, when the two are not one and the same.

PRODUCTION QUANTITIES

The block diagram of Figure 7–2 serves for general comparisons of different production runs, both of conventional and NC types. The quantities given can be approximate only, and are based on total or annual requirements of some particular part. The quantities may coincide with the lot sizes, or they may involve a number of individual runs or lots. The numerical control portion of the diagram applies chiefly to point-to-point control.

Small quantities or small-volume production—it may involve up to 25, 50 or 100 parts, depending also on types of part and machine—is also variously referred to as small-lot production, job lots, batch production, or small custom lots.

A COMPARISON OF NUMERICALLY CONTROLLED AND TRACER MACHINING

Figure 7–3 shows a cost comparison among three different machines when producing the same part: conventionally or manually operated engine lathe, tracer controlled high production lathe, and NC lathe. The latter reference is to a Monarch Pathfinder numerically controlled lathe.

In this graph, by The Monarch Machine Tool Company, unit cost is plotted against the number of parts. The part is a 3.5 inch shaft of AISI 4145 steel.

In Figure 7–3, note that:

1. For one part only, the template cost in this case makes the entire cost per part for the tracer lathe the highest, at $112.87. The NC lathe comes next at $54.84, and then the engine lathe at $21.71. For a single part, the engine lathe method is the cheapest in this example.

2. At approximately 1,000 parts, the template cost for this shaft has been written off, and the per-piece cost—$0.36—is now the same as by the NC lathe. From this point on, or for higher volumes, the tracer controlled lathe is more economical, due to its faster cycle as well as lower initial investment cost.

3. At 10 parts, the numerical control method is cheaper than both the engine and tracer lathe methods, and at 1,000 parts, the engine lathe is far behind, at $0.76 per piece,

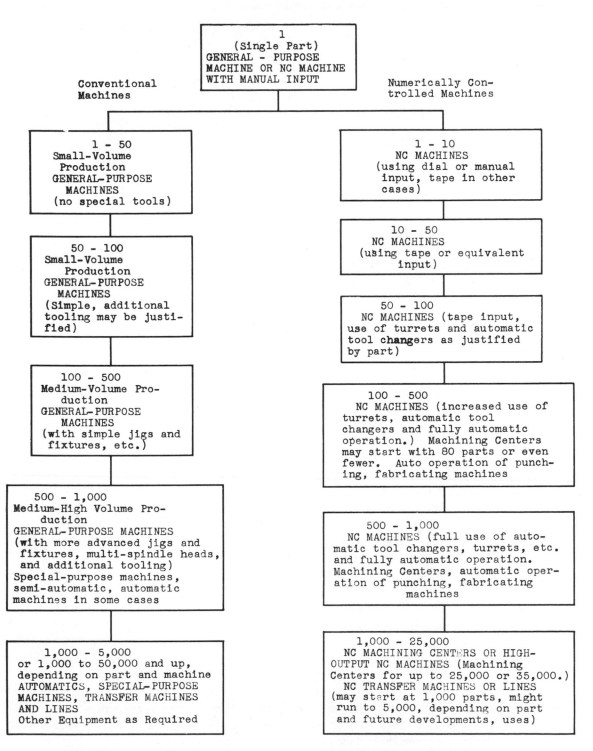

Figure 7–2. Approximate annual production quantities, number of parts, that may be used in conventional and numerically controlled processing.

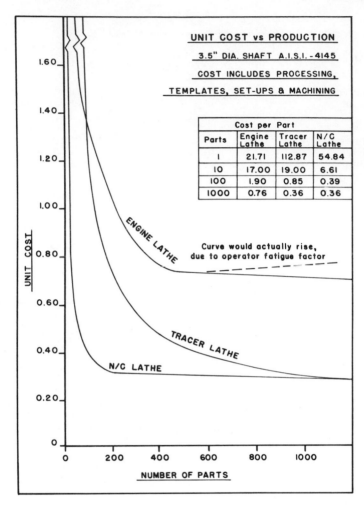

Figure 7–3. Cost comparison for turning a shaft by three
different methods. (The Monarch Machine Tool Co.)

while tracer and numerically controlled machining have both dropped to $0.36 per part. Further comparisons between different, alternative methods are given in Chapter 13.

Economic Lot Sizes for NC Processing

In determining economic lot sizes and in cost estimating in general for NC manufacturing, each type of part must usually be treated on its own merits, according to its own particular conditions. Some general rules, however, can be presented. As stated, an entire order may be run off in one lot, but more frequently, the total quantity required in a year or for an order, may be produced in several lots spaced throughout a year. In the latter case, the setup costs are multiplied by the number of runs or lots.

COMPARING SMALL LOTS OF BOTH TYPES

In conventional machining, charges against parts in storage or inventory must be balanced against the costs of frequent setups, and all other individual factors must be considered, in establishing maximum and minimum levels of inventory. In numerically controlled machining or processing, the setup costs are drastically cut, allowing a new and different inventory policy to be adopted, as shown.

In conventional machining, in small quantities of up to 50 pieces a year, for instance (which might be five separate lots of 10 pieces each), when no additional special tooling is justified, the last few parts in a lot cost almost as much as the first few—because they are individually and "manually" produced.

The time taken and the cost per piece remain practically the same, at least once a certain point on the learning curve has been reached by the operator. The hourly output, therefore, cannot be increased under manual operation, if all factors are constant.

In setting lot sizes for numerically controlled production, quantities can be smaller, because operator skill and setup times are not such important criteria.

REPRESENTATIVE NC ECONOMIC LOT SIZES

In a series of case studies, seven cases involving vertical NC drilling, boring and tapping machines, turret drills, and a vertical milling machine doing similar work, the average lot size was 37 pieces, the average number of pieces or quantity required per year was 204, and the average number of lots per year was 4.

On some tape controlled turret drills with automatic control of spindle and turret, small lots of about 5 to 10 pieces may be machined manually, i.e., without full automatic control.

From 10 to 25 parts is not too small a run for automatic tool changing machines; medium lots can range to 200 parts for machining and to 500 in fast punch press operations. Runs are not limited to these quantities in order to be competitive with various conventional methods.

Using NC machining centers, with numerous tools available on tape command, lots of 10 to nearly 1,000 of applicable parts can show substantial cost reductions compared with production on general-purpose machines.

FORMULA FOR ECONOMIC LOT SIZES

No single formula for economic lot sizes is likely to satisfy every requirement, but the following one, given by The Cincinnati Milling Machine Company,[1] is one method for determining the most economical lot size:

$$C = \sqrt{\frac{200\ AS}{i(L+M)}}, \text{ in which:}$$

$C =$ Most economical lot size (units)
$A =$ Annual number required (units)
$S =$ Cost per setup ($)
$i =$ Annual inventory carrying cost (%)
$L =$ Unit labor costs ($)
$M =$ Unit material costs ($).

---

[1] *The Economics of Numerical Control*, in *Acramatic Numerical Control—Reprinted from Report from Cincinnati Milling* (Cincinnati, Ohio: Cimtrol Division, The Cincinnati Milling Machine Company, ca. 1960), p. 7.

Method Suggested by PERA for Determining the Most Economical Production Method

The Production Engineering Research Association (PERA) of Great Britain has developed a procedure for determining the most economical production method,[2] details of which are given here by permission.

The PERA states in its report that there was a need for a quick method to determine the most economical production method. The salient points of the PERA method are:

1. Absence of any attempt to base the method on component geometry, because others had found this approach unsuccessful.

2. Information which is available or can be obtained in most manufacturing plants is used instead of the component-geometry approach.

3. The method arrived at is based on conventional production costs and times, and their ratio to those applying in the case of numerically controlled methods.

4. The calculations are simplied by the use of nomograms.

5. Since this method is applicable to any two methods of production, no reference to numerical control has been made in the nomograms, the PERA points out.

BREAK-EVEN QUANTITY q

The cost C for producing q components is given by:

$$C = T + q(tM + A);\qquad(1)$$

where T = pre-production cost, i.e., cost of programming, planning, design and manufacture of jigs and tools;

t = machining time (floor-to-floor);

M = machine hour rate (i.e., depreciation rate, plus labor rate plus overhead rate);

A = cost per component, of inspection (off the machine), fitting and assembly.

Let the suffixes c and n indicate conventional and numerically controlled methods respectively.

Then for conventional production:

$$C_c = T_c + q(t_cM_c + A_c);\qquad(2)$$

and for production by numerically controlled methods:

$$C_n = T_n + q(t_nM_n + A_n).\qquad(3)$$

Now if $C_c = C_n$,

then:

$$T_c + q(t_cM_c + A_c) = T_n + q(t_nM_n + A_n).\qquad(4)$$

Therefore, q, the break-even quantity, is given by:

$$q = \frac{T_c - T_n}{(t_nM_n + A_n) - (t_cM_c + A_c)}.\qquad(5)$$

Examination of this equation reveals that the numerator is the difference of the pre-production costs, and the denominator the difference of the processing costs.

If we now let $P_n = (t_nM_n + A)$, and $P_c = (t_cM_c + A_c)$;

equation (5) becomes:

$$q = \frac{T_c - T_n}{P_n - P_c}.\qquad(6)$$

Since both $(T_c - T_n)$ and $(P_n - P_c)$ can be either positive or negative, the value of q can be interpreted in four different ways, and these are:

Case 1. When the pre-production costs are greater for conventional manufacture than by numerically controlled methods, i.e., $(T_c - T_n)$ is positive; but the processing cost per part is smaller by the conventional method, i.e., $(P_n - P_c)$ is positive. Then q has a positive value [represented as q + ve in

[2] Numerical Control—An Economic Survey, (PERA) Report No. 119 (Melton Mowbray, Leicestershire, England: Production Engineering Research Association of Great Britain, Nov., 1963) pp. 33–37.

diagram on the four cases, to follow], below which it is more economical to produce by numerically controlled methods, and above which it is economical to use conventional means.

Case 2. When $(T_c - T_n)$ is positive, and $(P_n - P_c)$ is negative (i.e., the process cost per component is greater by conventional methods) then q is negative (i.e., less than zero) and therefore it is always more economical to produce by numerically controlled methods.

Case 3. When $(T_c - T_n)$ is negative, i.e., $T_n > T_c$, and $P_n - P_c$ is positive (i.e., $P_n > P_c$), then q is negative (i.e., less than zero), and it is always cheaper to produce by conventional methods.

Case 4. When $(T_c - T_n)$ is negative, i.e., $T_n > T_c$ but $(P_n - P_c)$ is negative, i.e., $P_c > P_n$, then q again has a positive value above which it is cheaper to use numerically controlled methods, and below which it is cheaper to use conventional means.

BREAK-EVEN NOMOGRAM

In order to simplify the determination of the break-even quantity, q, a nomogram has been constructed for the solution of equations (5) and (6). The basic form of the nomogram is shown in Figure 7–4. The range of the nomogram may be varied provided the following relationship is maintained:

$$q \propto \frac{S_1}{S_2};$$

where S_1 = difference in pre-production costs, units/inch,

* S_2 = difference in process costs per component, units/inch.*

[In this relationship, q varies as $\frac{S_1}{S_2}$, as shown.]

The four cases for the interpretation of q are set out in Figure 7–5.

Nomograms incorporating actual values are constructed after calculations based on the preceding are made. To use a nomogram, it is necessary to join the points representing $(T_c - T_n)$ and $(P_n - P_c)$ on the vertical axes by a straight line. The break-even quantity, q, is the point where this straight line intersects the diagonal of the nomogram.

Additional Factors

OTHER FACTORS THAT DETERMINE LIMITS

In establishing limits for the use of numerical control, it must be remembered that not all of the gains are to be found on the production floor. The factors of manufacturing control by management, more uniform quality, reduced lead time, faster setups, and others, as treated in previous chapters, must be given required consideration.

SPECIAL USES AND REQUIREMENTS

Special and additional uses for numerical control may be found: for example, using point-to-point control for a quick inspection of a part (using dial input, if necessary), and employing numerical control equipment to test a parts-programming system.

Requirements can also vary as to part size—a small plant having, for example, fewer than 250 employees, and a medium plant, say with 250 to 1,000 workers, may place more emphasis on the flexibility aspect of automation by numerical control than large plants of more than 1,000 men in the plant force and with conventional automation. And in number, it is the small and medium plants that predominate.

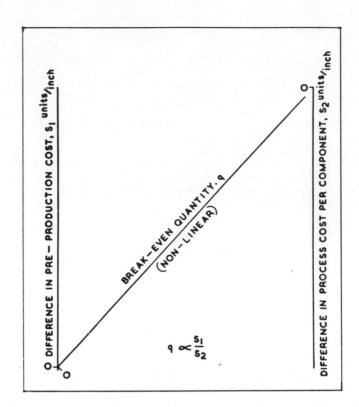

Figures 7–4 & 7–5. At top: Structure of break-even nomogram for determining the most economical production method. (Production Engineering Research Association.) At bottom: The four cases for interpreting the value of q, the break-even quantity. (Production Engineering Research Association.)

PRE-PRODUCTION COST / PROCESS COST	$T_c > T_n$ $\left[T_c - T_n\right]$ +ve	$T_n > T_c$ $\left[T_c - T_n\right]$ −ve
$P_n > P_c$ $\left[P_n - P_c\right]$ +ve	**CASE 1.** q +ve	**CASE 3.** q −ve CONVENTIONAL METHOD ALWAYS MORE ECONOMICAL
$P_c > P_n$ $\left[P_n - P_c\right]$ −ve	**CASE 2.** q −ve NUMERICAL CONTROL ALWAYS MORE ECONOMICAL	**CASE 4.** q +ve

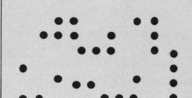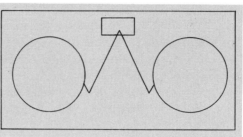

CHAPTER EIGHT

APPROACHING THE INVESTMENT
IN NUMERICAL CONTROL

THE ECONOMICS OF CAPITAL INVESTMENT IN NUMERICAL CONTROL IN-
VOLVE BOTH FINANCIAL FACTORS AND TECHNICAL
CONSIDERATIONS (EQUIPMENT SELECTION), THE
FORMER CULMINATING IN THE DESIRED ANNUAL RE-
TURN ON INVESTMENT OR A PREDETERMINED PAYOFF
PERIOD. (FOR TECHNICAL FACTORS OF MACHINE AND
SYSTEM SELECTION, SEE CHAPTER 10.)

BOTH OF THESE AREAS ARE IMPORTANT IN THE
JUSTIFICATION OF NUMERICAL CONTROL: THE TECH-
NICAL AREA BECAUSE A NEW CONCEPT OF MANUFAC-
TURING IS TO BE CONSIDERED, AND THE FINANCIAL
AREA BECAUSE AVAILABLE INVESTMENT FUNDS ARE
HAVING INCREASING DEMANDS PLACED UPON THEM
FOR OTHER PURPOSES BESIDES THEIR INVESTMENT
IN MACHINE TOOLS OR OTHER CAPITAL EQUIPMENT.
FURTHER, NC EQUIPMENT REQUIRES A LARGER OUT-
LAY THAN THE CONVENTIONAL TYPE.

Differences Between Investing in Numerical Control and in Conventional Equipment

There are certain essential differences between investment in numerical control equipment and in new equipment *per se*. The advantages and characteristics of numerical control—which account for the differences—must be duly weighed, aside from considering the usual advantages of improved performance that go with new or improved conventional machines.

The introduction of numerical control affects practically all levels of management, engineering and production; therefore, all departments should be consulted when the choice and investment are made. This helps to assure that support for the new manufacturing concept and program will be given by all concerned. Investing in NC equipment is not comparable to conventional replacement or purchase of machines.

The economic evaluation or justification of numerical control additionally involves factors such as machine replacement and depreciation policies, the method of acquiring the equipment, and other related considerations, which are also present when conventional production machinery is purchased.

Why New Machine Purchases Are Made

The reasons for purchasing new machine tools and other production equipment can vary widely, and are summarized in Table 4.

TABLE 4

REASONS FOR INVESTING IN NEW PRODUCTION EQUIPMENT

REASON FOR INVESTMENT	REMARKS
1. New Manufacturing Program or New Plant	Involves acquisition of all required equipment.
2. Company or Plant Expansion Program	May involve establishment of entirely new, additional production lines, or adding of individual machines.
3. Obsolescence (of one or more Types)	Obsolescence can refer to: (1) obsolescence of machine tool or production unit, making economical or profitable production impossible; (2) obsolete product—the market for which has disappeared; (3) obsolete or out-of-date manufacturing process; and (4) disappearance of market for a product due to change in consumer or capital equipment requirements, aside from the product obsolescence standpoint.
4. Deterioration or Expiry of Useful Service Life of Machine	With machine tools, and present advances in technology, production machines generally become obsolete before they become worn out; some rebuilding may or may not have been done in the meantime.
5. Need for Increased Degree of Automation	More automation may be required due to a shortage of skilled labor for general purpose machines, to provide more economical output, to increase the competitive position, or to increase total output.
6. New Manufacturing Processes	New equipment is generally required if entirely new manufacturing processes are to be added to a plant's operations.
7. The Necessity to Extend Range and Variety of Work Performed in Plant	New equipment may meet varied demands of production aside from those of quantity.
8. Changing or Adding to Character of Manufacturing Plant or Machinery	To meet production schedules, faster deliveries, or better fulfilment of contracts, equipment providing greater flexibility, for example, or having additional features, may be required.
9. Overload of Orders or Resumption of Previous Subcontract Work in Prime Contractor's Plant	An increasing work schedule and less dependence on subcontracting may require additional capacity, and conversely, a subcontractor may be faced with production overloads.

In connection with Table 4, numerical control should be given due consideration in each case, and it warrants particular consideration for reasons No. 1–5 inclusive, and No. 8.

Acquisition Methods

Numerically controlled equipment may be acquired through any one of the following methods:

1. Outright purchase. This may also include a trade-in allowance.
2. Deferred or time payment plans.
3. Leasing or rental plans.
4. Leasing plans with options to buy.

Most if not all of these methods are available for purchases from major machine tool or other production equipment builders, or/and in conjunction with industrial financing corporations or institutions.

Gradual Approach or Total Concept of Numerical Control?

Involved in the capital investment of numerically controlled machines may be the purchase of single units or a larger number of machines, or an entirely new production line may have to be set up. Whether such a production line (e.g., transfer line) should be of NC type, or whether numerically controlled and conventional machine tools should be installed in a new line or when major changes are made, the planning calls for important decisions.

With any new production line or facility, should you "go all-out" for numerical control or mix individual NC machines with conventional equipment? There is no single straight answer, although strong arguments can be made for the all-out or total approach.

Many firms however, prefer to phase into numerical control gradually. This can be done through making use of alternatives as provided on various numerically controlled equipment (as described in other chapters of this book), or by obtaining only one or a few machines at a time. For a small plant, the gradual approach may mean a single-spindle NC drill, with perhaps straight-line milling capability, instead of a machining center with automatic tool changer.

PROGRAMMING AN IMPORTANT FACTOR

Programming methods and facilities must also be considered. For general positioning control, although computer programming is not necessary, it can save time if many orders must be processed in a short space of time. Custom computer programming facilities are available, and a computer need not be acquired unless it can be justified by the amount of work it will be called upon to do—and then it may share this work with other operations carried out within a company.

For large-scale numerical control applications, especially where considerable continuous-path machining is to be carried out or when similar systems are employed, then computer programming facilities and the complete or nearly complete numerical control approach should be considered together. Unless the plant or operation is extremely large, however, a new programming staff or organization is usually not required: the existing process planning or methods engineering department can readily undertake numerical control programming, with or without computer-assisted programming. Once the procedures are set up, the detail programming and tape preparation can often be assigned to others; and accomplished with the use of relatively inexpensive tape punching or preparation equipment.

Whether numerical control should be adopted in stages, or embarked upon on a large scale, depends so much on the individual circumstances that no specific rules can be laid down. When new plants or new products are to be launched, or entirely new production lines are to be set up, as already noted, then the total or complete numerical control approach may be the preferable one, again depending on the degree of flexibility that is required, the market requirements, and so on, comparing each factor with the corresponding one of conventional equipment, where applicable.

It is important at the same time to plan for the probable requirements for years ahead, to avoid possibly disastrous future results. A plant must be able to cope with future production demands, the requirements of greater accuracy, the tightening of tolerances, or the necessity of increased flexibility in manufacturing.

The Obsolescence Factor in Equipment Selection

Since obsolescence of equipment (see Table 4 again) is usually the most frequent cause in replacing machine tools, the obsolescence factor of new equipment, when purchasing it, must also be considered. Numerically controlled machines are less likely to become out-of-date in a given time than conventional machines.

As for the possible obsolescence factor of the NC machines themselves, it can be stated that the designs have been well established by this time, and although improvements and changes continue to be made, the shorter payoff period for NC equipment, due to its higher productivity, considerably lessens the danger and effects of obsolescence. Since capital costs of this equipment have also come down, the obsolescence risk should be proportionately far less than with conventional machine tools or other production equipment.

If early obsolescence appears to be a danger in the purchase of the equipment, then leasing instead of purchasing can be considered, or as another alternative, leasing with an option to buy.

Depreciation Policy and Capital Investment

The depreciation factor is important in all investment of capital equipment and manufacturing facilities, and in machinery replacement policies and formulas. First, depreciation on machinery can be deducted from taxable income, and second, the funds saved can make provision for a regular replacement policy to keep equipment up-to-date and economically productive. These funds should be used to replace both worn out and obsolete equipment.

A program of capital investment in numerically controlled machine tools and in general machine replacement must include an advantageous depreciation policy. The two cannot be separated without needless financial losses. This is particularly important with numerical control, because of the higher capital investment involved.

A policy of pursuing a well thought-out machine depreciation plan, within the limits of United States Treasury Department provisions and regulations, is of utmost importance not only to the financial officers of a company but also to operating management and production engineering personnel. More favorable depreciation rates—largely because of shortened "useful lives" of machinery, for depreciation purposes—have made it possible for many companies to depreciate their machine tools over a 10-year period instead of the former 20-year span they employed. Investment tax credits have been another important factor in developing capital investment programs. Keeping up-to-date with current and changing Treasury Department regulations is therefore a continuing requirement.[1]

Equipment is depreciated down to its salvage value, which may be 10% for general calculations. Several methods of computing depreciation are provided, but "no asset may be depreciated below a reasonable salvage value under any method," according to Treasury Department rules. In computing depreciation, it is permissible to take into account obsolescence caused by technological improvements which shorten the useful life of the machinery or equipment in question.

The useful life, the method and rate of depreciation, and the salvage value, are of course dependent on written agreement with the Internal Revenue Service of the United States Treasury Department, and must be based on the individual requirements, within prescribed guidelines for depreciation. Any available incentives, and additional possible deductions, should be ascertained on a current basis.

Machine tool builders have made time payment plans available, based on government investment tax credits. In one example of a machine tool purchase plan, the builder accepted a down payment equal to a current 7% investment tax credit, and newer, shortened useful lives of production machinery for depreciation purposes were also taken into account.

DEPRECIATION METHODS

Three methods for computing depreciation have been in general use: the straight-line method, which is the simplest; the double-declining balance method; and the sum-of-the-years digits method. The latter two give the highest depreciation allowances for the first few years of an investment.

Straight-Line Method—In this depreciation method, equal amounts are depreciated over a given period of years. If a machine tool qualifies for a 10-year useful life, for example, and is valued at $10,000, the amounts written off or depreciated each year would be $1,000. (This is a simple example only; salvage value, and a first-year additional depreciation which may be applicable, have not been included.) The machine cost, less its salvage value, is generally deducted in equal annual amounts over the period of its estimated useful life.

Double-Declining Balance Method—In this method, the depreciation is calculated on the balance, or the reduced undepreciated cost, and the rate is double that of the straight-line depreciation method. For example, if the 10% annual rate is applicable, as may be determined by the Treasury provisions, then, on a $10,000 machine, for instance, the depreciation for the first year would be 20%, or $2,000, leaving an undepreciated cost or undepreciated balance of $8,000. In the second year, the depreciation would be 20% of the balance of $8,000, or $1,600, and so on.

This method has been applicable to assets having a useful life of three years or more; it comes under the "declining balance" method, and twice the rate used under the straight-line

---

[1] Examples: A much more favorable atmosphere for the replacement of capital equipment and for plant modernization was provided by the U. S. Treasury Department, Internal Revenue Service depreciation provisions introduced in mid-1962, known as Revenue Procedure 62–21 [RP 62–21]). This is also known as Internal Revenue Publication No. 456, having the title *Depreciation Guidelines and Rules.* These new rules superseded both the old and the later versions of Bulletin "F."

At the same time, a 7% Investment Tax Credit was instituted, allowing a company to reduce its tax by as much as 7% of the amount spent annually on new equipment. (In connection with RP 62–21, it should be noted that the still later publication by the U. S. Treasury Department, Publication No. 457, with the title, *Tables for Applying Revenue Procedure 62–21,* contained three tables that superseded the three illustrative tables in Publication No. 456.)

The changed regulations allowed shorter useful lives for depreciation purposes; a representative machine tool could be written off over 12 years instead of 16 years under the previous rules.

method has been the maximum that could be employed. In some cases, 1½ times has been the maximum.

With this method, the amount of depreciation deducted becomes smaller each year, but the first few years give a much faster writeoff—which is important for production machinery or equipment—than the straight-line method.

It has been possible to change to the straight-line method at any time during the useful life of the property, with consent of the Internal Revenue Service. "Salvage value is not deducted from the cost or other basis of your property in determining the annual depreciation allowance under this method. You must not, however, depreciate your property below an amount equal to the reasonable salvage value of such property," stated IRS regulations.[1]

Since the amounts deducted under the double-declining balance method become quite small in the latter years, and the depreciation would carry on almost indefinitely with ever-reduced amounts, conversion of the depreciation policy to straight-line depreciation after the optimum deductions have been made under the double-declining balance method, is therefore a preferable solution.

When changing from the double-declining balance method to the straight-line method, consent of the Internal Revenue Service has not been required in the recent past, provided there was no conflict with any written agreement as to the established useful life and the depreciation. If the switch was made after 5 years of a 10-year depreciation period, the salvage value generally had to be deducted first from the undepreciated balance, and the latter written off in five equal or approximately equal annual instalments.

To keep abreast of details, and the changes that may be made, contact with the Internal Revenue Service should always be maintained in this connection.

Sum-of-The-Years Digits Method—This depreciation procedure is entirely different from the two preceding ones. First, the numbers or digits representing each year of the useful life are added. If the useful life for depreciation is 10 years, the sum of the figures representing each of the years comes to 55. The depreciation for any one year is a fraction of the total cost, having the year as the numerator and the total number of years as the denominator. These fractions however, are used in their reverse order.

For example, were a $10,000 machine to be depreciated, using a 10-year depreciation period, the fraction for the first year would be 10/55, and the amount, $1,818. For the second year, the depreciation would be 9/55 of $10,000, or $1,636. This process is continued, using the fractions in their reverse order, until, at the end of 10 years, the total cost, or 55/55 of $10,000, is depreciated.

The total cost or other basis used for this method, under the existing regulations, must be reduced by the estimated salvage value for purposes of computing the depreciation; in addition, the years-digits method may be used only on property which meets the requirements for twice the straight-line rate of the declining-balance method. As for the salvage factor in the double-declining balance method (declining-balance method), this value is not deducted from the cost or basis for computing purposes, but the depreciation must stop when the estimated salvage value is reached.

Additional methods of depreciation may be possible as alternative choices, as may be determined with the Internal Revenue Service upon individual application.

Comparison Table of Depreciation Methods—Table 5 compares three methods of depreciation by showing both the deductions for depreciation which may be made annually for income tax, and the accumulated depreciation or recovery.

---

[1] Document No. 5050 (12-62).

The straight-line depreciation method is quite simple in principle; therefore, it is not included in the table; for a useful life of 10 years for a machine, a unit cost of $1,000 would be depreciated annually at 10% of the total cost, or at $100. As can be seen from the table, this approach provides much less in depreciation deductions during the first four years, and in the case of the sum-of-the-years digits method, the larger reduction is carried into the fifth year—it is more than $109, compared with $100 under the straight-line method.

In the third pair of columns in Table 5, the double-declining balance method is replaced at the end of the fifth year by the straight-line method; the balance of $327.60 to be recovered is then dealt with in five annual instalments of $65.50 each, except for $65.60, as adjusted, for the sixth year. The table, of course, is based on a unit cost of $1,000.

From the annual deduction figures shown for the double declining-balance method, it can be seen that the deductions can be converted to percentages of the original unit cost by dividing each by 10. For example, during the second year, the deduction for a depreciation of $160 represents 16% of the original cost, the third year the deduction represents 12.8%, and the tenth year, 2.68%.

TABLE 5

COMPARISON OF DEPRECIATION METHODS

DOUBLE-DECLINING BALANCE		SUM-OF-THE-YEARS DIGITS METHOD		DOUBLE-DECLINING BALANCE FOR FIRST 5 YEARS, STRAIGHT-LINE FOR SECOND 5 YEARS	
ANNUAL DEPRECIATION OR DEDUCTION	ACCUMULATED DEPRECIATION OR RECOVERY	ANNUAL DEPRECIATION OR DEDUCTION	ACCUMULATED DEPRECIATION OR RECOVERY	ANNUAL DEPRECIATION OR DEDUCTION	ACCUMULATED DEPRECIATION OR RECOVERY
$200.00	$200.00	$181.80	$181.80	$200.00	$200.00
160.00	360.00	163.60	345.40	160.00	360.00
128.00	488.00	145.50	490.90	128.00	488.00
102.40	590.40	127.30	618.20	102.40	590.40
81.90	672.30	109.10	727.30	82.00	672.40
65.50	737.80	90.90	818.20	65.60	738.00
52.40	790.20	72.70	890.90	65.50	803.50
42.00	832.20	54.50	945.40	65.50	869.00
33.60	865.80	36.40	981.80	65.50	934.50
26.80	892.60	18.20	1,000.00	65.50	1,000.00
$892.60		$1,000.00		$1,000.00	

OTHER DEPRECIATION FACTORS

All aspects of depreciation regulations cannot be included here. For example, the *reserve ratio test* was intended to establish whether a company's depreciation claims were reconcilable with its actual modernization and replacement policy. Regulations may be changed, however, and such information must of course be kept up-to-date. The funds saved on income tax, through depreciation, should be applied toward such modernization and replacement. The accelerated depreciation methods are preferable for writing off NC equipment, as with most other machinery.

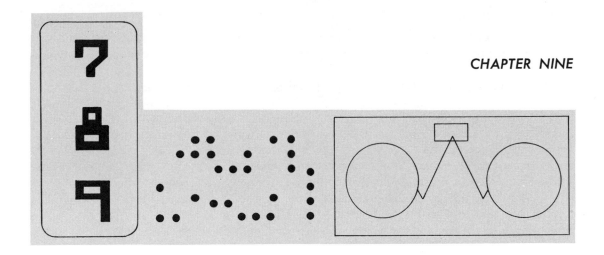

CHAPTER NINE

MAKING AN ECONOMIC EVALUATION
TO DETERMINE PAYOFF

IN JUSTIFYING NEW PRODUCTION EQUIPMENT, IN CHOOSING A MACHINE INVESTMENT PROGRAM OR A MACHINE REPLACEMENT POLICY, DIRECT LABOR COSTS ARE FREQUENTLY THE PRIME CONSIDERATION. IN MANY YEARS, WORKER PRODUCTIVITY OR OUTPUT PER MAN-HOUR HAS RISEN MORE SLOWLY THAN AVERAGE HOURLY EARNINGS. IT IS THEREFORE NOT SURPRISING THAT MANUFACTURING INDUSTRIES ARE TURNING MORE AND MORE TO AUTOMATION. MOREOVER, THE ADVANCES OF TECHNOLOGICAL CHANGE AND PROGRESS WILL NOT BE STEMMED, AS HISTORY HAS SHOWN.

LABOR SAVINGS HOWEVER, ARE NOT THE ONLY REASON FOR ADOPTING THE NUMERICAL CONTROL FORM OF AUTOMATION, ALTHOUGH SUCH SAVINGS CAN BE SUBSTANTIAL. WHERE LAGGING PRODUCTIVITY FIGURES ARE QUOTED, OBSOLESCENCE OF EQUIPMENT MAY ALSO BE A CONTRIBUTING FACTOR.

DIRECT LABOR SAVINGS, TAKING INTO ACCOUNT

the increases in the number of parts produced per hour and the hourly wage rates, are generally readily calculated and the old figures compared with the new or projected ones.

Formulas and Justification for Capital Investment in Machinery

Most formulas used in justifying an investment in production machinery, or for use in machine replacement programs, belong to either one of two general approaches: the payback or payoff period—the number of years in which a machine will pay for itself—and the annual return on investment that is expected to result. One approach is, in effect, the reverse of the other. The general formulas may be listed as follows, in simplified form.

1. Payback, or the payoff period as simple payback, which can be stated as Invested Capital/Net Annual Income. This can also be expressed as investment divided by the increase in annual income or, in effect, the net savings derived from the investment in the equipment.

Payback or payout is also expressed as Capital Cost of Machine/Direct Labor Savings Less Total Operating Costs.

2. Return on investment, or simple return on investment, can be given as Net Annual Income/Invested Capital, in simple form.

3. The discounted cash flow method is also known as the time-adjusted return on investment. This approach is in effect based on the realization that, for example, $1,000 in cash now, is worth more than $1,000 paid in 10 annual instalments of $100 each, because it can be invested to draw interest. Compound interest is also taken into account.

"Cash flow" can be defined in several ways, but generally speaking, may be regarded basically as profit after costs and after taxes, plus depreciation allowances.

4. The improved MAPI formula, by the Machinery and Allied Products Institute, Washington, D. C., has been specially evolved for justifying capital investments in the replacement of machinery or production facilities. It will be described in a separate section of this chapter.

Any formula selected involves detailed calculations of all the factors to be considered. It must be admitted however, that some plants frequently purchase new equipment without any elaborate formula computations, but base their decisions on their general and immediate requirements only, or upon their general long-term requirements.

Example of Payback with an NC Machine

The following is an example of justifying the purchase of a numerically controlled machine based on savings in direct labor and in tooling. When the savings from these two factors are not considered sufficient to justify the investment, then additional factors, as will be shown, are taken into consideration. The machine involved performs a variety of machining operations, has an automatic tool changer, and costs $82,000.

COMPUTING DIRECT LABOR COST SAVINGS

On typical groups of parts, required in quantities of 25 to 125 per group per year, the time per part, involving three existing machines, is 3.01 hours. The direct labor cost per part, at $3.00 per hour, including fringe benefits, is therefore $9.03.

Using the new numerically controlled machine, the time per part is 0.91 hours, and direct labor cost per part, $2.73, at the same rate of $3.00 an hour. The direct labor cost saving per part is the difference, or $6.30.

With a machine utilization factor of 90%, the savings per year, for one-shift operation, or 2080 hours, are:

90/100 × 2080/0.91 × $6.30 = $12,960.

Since a numerically controlled machine with this type of output and with the investment represented, should be operated on at least two shifts, if possible, the total direct labor cost savings for two-shift operation are therefore $25,920.

SAVINGS IN TOOLING COSTS

The annual savings in tooling costs, mostly on jigs and fixtures, amount to $7,250, and these can be regarded as conservative savings.

The total savings based only on the two factors of direct labor and tooling, are therefore $25,920 plus $7,250, or $33,170.

Simplified calculations for payback and annual recovery (not including interest on the cash flow), follow. The double-declining balance method of calculating depreciation allowances is used, expressed in this case as straight percentages of the original cost. A straight 50% tax is taken in this example.

First Year:
 (1) Depreciation at 20% of $82,000 = $16,400
 (2) Savings less depreciation, or
    $33,170 — $16,400 = $16,770
 (3) 50% tax on savings less depreciation, or
    50/100 × $16,700 = $8,385
 (4) Cash recovery at end of first year;
    $33,170 — $8,385 = $24,785 .... $24,785

Second Year:
 Depreciation at 16% of $82,000 = $13,120
 Cash recovery (simplified method) or
    $33,170 — 50/100 ($33,170 — $13,120) = $23,145 23,145
 Using the depreciation factor first, and taking the savings balance as 50% after tax, this
    may also be expressed as:
    $13,120 + [50/100 (33,170 — $13,120)] = $23,145.

Third Year:
 Depreciation at 12.8% of $82,000 = $10,496
 Cash recovery, or $33,170 — 50/100 ($33,170 — $10,496)
    = $21,833 21,833

Fourth Year:
 Depreciation at 10.24% of $82,000 = $8,397
 Cash recovery equals $33,170 — 50/100 ($33,170 — $8,397)
    = $20,784 20,784

Total recovery in four years $90,547

The $82,000 numerically controlled machine is paid off in less than four years, based on two savings factors only—direct labor cost savings and savings in tooling. If these two savings were insufficient to assure an early payoff, then additional factors such as savings in indirect labor costs, plant space, and power requirements, and savings from the other advantages inherent in numerical control, must be calculated or estimated to justify the investment and to assure a satisfactory payback period.

FACTORS FOR ANALYZING A MACHINE INVESTMENT OR REPLACEMENT

All of the factors involved in making an analysis for capital investment in a conventional new machine or production line, or in machinery replacement, must likewise be included in justifying an investment in numerically controlled equipment, especially if savings in direct labor costs and tooling are not sufficient to assure the desired annual rate of return on investment or do not result in the planned payback period.

It is important that no factor be ignored in carrying out such an analysis for justification, and in the case of replacements, it is made in comparison with conventional equipment or the existing machine that is to be replaced. The full effects of fringe benefits (which may run as high as 20% or more of the straight pay roll), depreciation, insurance, and taxes, are sometimes given insufficient attention.

The chief factors are given in Table 6, and more could be added to these to suit an individual plant's requirements. All such factors must be considered for or against the investment or replacement; usually an improvement is sought in each factor, although factors such as insurance and taxes will generally be higher with the new machine.

TABLE 6

FACTORS FOR A MACHINE INVESTMENT ANALYSIS OR REPLACEMENT PROGRAM

ADVANTAGE REQUIRED OR FACTOR TO BE CONSIDERED

Increased Output

Higher Machine Utilization Time

Improved Accuracy

Reduction in Direct Labor Costs (including all fringe benefits)

Indirect Labor Cost Savings

Reduced Tooling Costs

Lower Obsolescence Factor

Advanced or Improved Technical Features

Flexibility in Production

Improved Scheduling Through Faster Output

Reduced Tool Inventory (for some machine or operations)

Less Scrap and Rework

Reduced Inspection Costs

Reduced Floor Space (a new machine replacing several others)

Reduced Maintenance or Down Time

Satisfactory Economic Life

Satisfactory Service Life

Power or Electric Energy Consumption (as related to output)

Improved Safety

Replacement of Two or More Machines (by One New Machine)

Reduction of Inventory (through improved and faster production and flexibility)

Faster Assembly of Parts Produced

Generally Improved Quality of Product

Any Other

DIRECT FINANCIAL CONSIDERATIONS

(as related to payback or main objectives)

Unit Cost

Freight Charges from Builder or Manufacturer to Plant

Depreciation (rate for income tax purposes is more favorable with new machines)

Insurance

Taxes (taxes and insurance generally higher with new machinery)

Resale Value of New Machine

Resale or Scrap Value of Old or Previous Machine

Financing or Acquisition Method

Installation Costs

Costs of any Special Utility Services or Special Environmental Conditions

Any Other

NUMERICAL CONTROL JUSTIFICATION FACTORS

In addition to considering the factors of Table 6, which are applicable generally, these factors should be adjusted where numerical control is concerned and compared with conventional equipment, as in Table 7. Further, there are the various inherent advantages of numerical control as dealt with in previous chapters, which, in many cases, may outweigh certain direct savings. With numerical control, not all factors can be expressed in dollars and cents.

TABLE 7

ADJUSTMENT FACTORS FOR NUMERICAL CONTROL
WHEN JUSTIFYING MACHINE INVESTMENT OR REPLACEMENT PROGRAMS

MANUFACTURING OR OPERATING FACTOR	ADJUSTMENT FACTOR AND REMARKS
1. Production Time per Part	Reduce by 25% to 80% or more, depending on individual conditions (compared with conventional machines).
2. Machine Utilization Time	Increase to 80% or 95% (utilization is at least two to three times that of conventionally operated machines).
3. Tooling Costs	Reduce by 30% to 90% (chiefly on jigs and fixtures, depending on nature of work and conditions).
4. Direct Labor Cost	Varies according to type of machine, number of conventional machines replaced, etc. (In general, per-piece labor cost as under "Production Time.") May reduce by 85% or more for fully automatic NC operation.
5. Indirect Labor Cost	Supervision, etc.—Reduce approximately as under "Direct Labor Cost."
6. Plant Space Requirements	Reduce according to number of machines replaced (NC operation may replace from 2 to 8 conventional machines, also depending on operations and conditions; frequently at least 2 machines replaced).
7. Other Factors and Additional Data (see text)	

DRASTIC REDUCTION IN OBSOLESCENCE

The problem of obsolescence virtually disappears in a numerically controlled production line, according to findings by the Construction Equipment Division, International Harvester Company (see Chapter 4, Case Study No. 6). Its flexibility makes the line readily adapted to future model changes in this case. Numerical control can go much further than the building block concept employed with many transfer lines to allow changes in the line as dictated by new models. Similarly, single NC machines also possess these advantages.

The Improved MAPI Formula for Machinery Replacement

The improved MAPI formula of the Machinery and Allied Products Institute and Council for Technological Advancement (Washington, D. C.), is basically intended as a detailed analysis and formula for machinery replacement.

When taking into account the characteristics of numerical control, the improved MAPI formula can be efficiently applied to projected numerically controlled installations as well. At the time of writing, no separate MAPI formula had been developed for numerically controlled equipment, which the regular formula is intended to or can cover also, although it can be regarded as a conservative approach where NC machines are involved.

SPECIAL FEATURES OF THE MAPI FORMULA

To stress the importance of purchasing an improved, more productive machine, and to realize optimum returns, the MAPI formula requires that a relatively high return on the investment must be obtained in the first year of the machine's use. This may mean, for example, that a conventionally operated machine may have to be replaced with an automatic one.

There are three main stages in applying the formula:

1. An analysis of the required investment.

2. A detailed analysis to establish the *next-year advantage* of the project. It includes: (a) the *operating advantage* during the first year after purchase, which evaluates all pertinent factors; (b) the *non-operating advantages*, which deals with certain advantages or points not connected with operation *per se;* and (c) the *total advantage*, which is the sum of (a) and (b) preceding.

3. A computation of the *MAPI urgency rating*. This establishes the urgency of the project, basically, by pinpointing the losses that would be incurred through a deferment of the purchase or investment. (See calculations and tables following, which give the MAPI urgency rating as Amount Available for Return on Investment/Net Investment Required; the resulting fraction or ratio is further multiplied by 100 to give percentage.)

An example of a MAPI analysis and evaluation, which would normally be accompanied by detailed work sheets, and which involves an automatic screw machine, follows. It also calls for the use of MAPI formulas or equations in full. As these are extremely lengthy, the MAPI (pronounced may-pie) charts are generally used instead (see footnote).[1]

MAPI CASE STUDY OF AN AUTOMATIC SCREW MACHINE

In this analysis,[2] an automatic screw machine is to be replaced, or studied for replacement by a newer, improved model.

The Project: A complete overhaul is required for a 39-year-old screw machine. The purchase of a newly designed automatic screw machine with a vertical slide and feeding arrangement as a better alternative is recommended by the equipment analyst. The project, installed, will cost $16,705. Complete overhauling of the old machine would cost $4,220, which is prorated over 10 years. The disposal value of the old or present machine is estimated at $300.

Analysis of Operating Advantage: The new machine is capable of greater speeds and can be tooled to take full advantage of them. After checking 11 jobs, the analyst estimates an average gain of 21%. Based on an 80-hour week (two-shift operation), this will produce a direct labor saving of 840 hours a year at $2.50 an hour (or at existing rate), of $2,100. Additional savings in fringe benefits will total $336. Further, decreases are expected in the following costs: scrap and rework, $600; maintenance, $1,055; and down time, $525.

Although the machine will produce faster than the one it is replacing, a work load beyond the 3,300 hours indicated as the operating rate is not available for the new machine. However, a value of $400 is assigned to the greater flexibility. The increase in property taxes and insurance is placed at $170.

STIPULATIONS:

Project operating rate	3,330 hr.
Projection pattern	Variant B [2]
(type of projection pattern for the absolute earnings	
of a depreciable asset)	
Service life	18 years
Terminal salvage ratio	5%
Tax depreciation method	Sum-of-digits
Tax rate	50%.

(See accompanying table "Summary of Analysis: Automatic Screw Machine.")

---

[1] George Terborgh, *Business Investment Policy—A MAPI Study and Manual* (Washington, D. C.: Machinery and Allied Products Institute and Council for Technological Advancement, copyright 1958, second printing, 1962), pp. 158–160.

[2] George Terborgh, *Business Investment Policy—A MAPI Study and Manual* (Washington, D. C.: Machinery and Allied Products Institute and Council for Technological Advancement, copyright 1958, second printing, 1962), pp. 71–73.

SUMMARY OF ANALYSIS

I. REQUIRED INVESTMENT

1. Installed Cost of Project	$16,705	1.
2. Disposal Value of Assets to be Retired by Project	300	2.
3. Capital Additions Required in Absence of Project	4,220	3.
4. Investment Released or Avoided by Project (2 + 3)	4,520	4.
5. Net Investment Required (1 — 4)	$12,185	5.

II. NEXT-YEAR ADVANTAGE FROM PROJECT

A. OPERATING ADVANTAGE

(USE FIRST YEAR OF PROJECT OPERATION)*

(Footnotes given at end of table.)

	INCREASE	DECREASE	
6. Assumed Operating Rate of Project (Hours per Year)		$ 3,300	6.
EFFECT OF PROJECT ON REVENUE			
7. From Change in Quality of Products	$	$	7.
8. From Change in Volume of Output			8.
9. Total	$ A	$ B	9.
EFFECT OF PROJECT ON OPERATING COSTS			
10. Direct Labor	$	$ 2,100	10.
11. Indirect Labor			11.
12. Fringe Benefits		336	12.
13. Maintenance		1,055	13.
14. Tooling			14.
15. Materials and Supplies			15.
16. Scrap and Rework		600	16.
17. Down Time		525	17.
18. Power			18.
19. Floor Space	$	$	19.
20. Property Taxes and Insurance	170		20.
21. Subcontracting			21.
22. Inventory			22.
23. Safety			23.
24. Flexibility		400	24.
25. Other			25.
26. Total	$ 170 A	$ 5,016 B	26.
27. Net Increase in Reveune (9A — 9B)		$	27.
28. Net Decrease in Operating Costs (26B — 26A)		$ 4,846	28.
29. Next-Year Operating Advantage (27 + 28)		$ 4,846	29.

* For projects with a significant break-in period, use performance after break-in.

B. NON-OPERATING ADVANTAGE

(Use only If There is An Entry in Line 4)

DECREASE

30. Next-Year Capital Consumption Avoided by Project: 30.
    A. Decline of Disposal Value During the Year $ A

    B. Next-Year Allocation of Capital Additions $ 422 B

                                          Total $ 422

C. TOTAL ADVANTAGE

31. Total Next-Year Advantage from Project (29 + 30) $ 5,268   31.

III. COMPUTATION OF MAPI URGENCY RATING

32. Total Next-Year Advantage After Income Tax (31-tax) $ 2,634   32.

33. MAPI Chart Allowance for Project (Total of Column F, following) $ 785 **   33.

(Enter Depreciable Assets Only)

Item or Group	Installed Cost of Item or Group	Estimated Service Life (Years)	Estimated Terminal Salvage (Percent of Cost)	MAPI Chart *** Number	Chart Percent-age	Chart Percent-age × Cost (E × A)
	A	B	C	D	E	F
Automatic Screw Machine	$16,705	18	5	3	4.7	$785
					Total	$ 785

34. Amount Available for Return on Investment (32 — 33) $ 1,849   34.

35. MAPI Urgency Rating (34 ÷ 5) · 100; (or, $\frac{1,849}{12,185}$ x 100)   %   15   35.

** Since the chart allowance does not cover future capital additions to project assets, add an annual proration of such additions, if any, to the figure in Line 33.

*** Refer to: George Terborgh, *Business Investment Policy—A MAPI Study and Manual* (Washington, D. C.: Machinery and Allied Products Institute and Council for Technological Advancement, copyright 1958, second printing, 1962), p. 125.

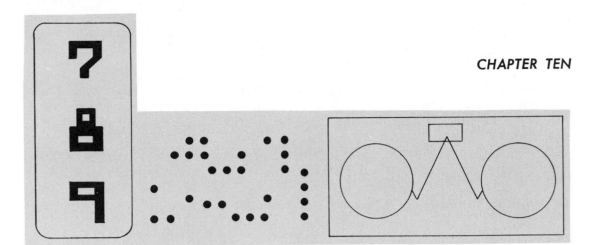

CHAPTER TEN

PLANNING IN ADVANCE
AND SELECTING EQUIPMENT

THE FULL SUPPORT OF ALL LEVELS OF MANAGEMENT AND OF ALL DEPART-
MENTS IN A COMPANY IS ESSENTIAL TO THE SUCCESS
OF NUMERICALLY CONTROLLED MANUFACTURING.

MOREOVER, THOSE ENTRUSTED WITH EFFECT-
ING THE NEW POLICY—WHETHER IT IS THE IN-
STALLATION OF A SINGLE MACHINE, AN NC
PRODUCTION LINE OR A LARGER NUMBER OF
MACHINES—MUST BE GIVEN FULL AUTHORITY FROM
HIGHEST COMPANY LEVELS TO CARRY IT OUT.

BRIEFING AND ORIENTATION CONFERENCES
SHOULD BE HELD WITH ALL DEPARTMENT HEADS
PRESENT, OR AS MAY BE INDICATED UNDER IN-
DIVIDUAL CIRCUMSTANCES, AND THEN SEPARATELY,
WITHIN EACH DEPARTMENT. THIS SHOULD BE FOL-
LOWED BY DETAILED PLANNING IN EACH DEPART-
MENT AND AT EACH LEVEL.

Advance Planning and Preparations

Plans and advance preparations should be complete, so that when the equipment arrives, production can start almost immediately after installation. This advance preparation should include not only the training of programmers and shop personnel, and their prior selection, but also the advance preparation of tapes for the jobs that are to be run, preparation of required tooling, and the setting up of a standard procedure for tape preparation and for the programming procedure as such.

Organizing Engineering Functions for Numerical Control

Although process planning or production engineering is not basically changed by the introduction of numerical control, its functions increase in importance and scope through the addition of tape programming and, of necessity, demand closer attention to detailed and effective planning.

DRAWINGS OR PRINTS

Process or production planning, tool designing, and programming, are closely interrelated. Engineering drawings or part prints (the responsibility of another department, product design engineering) should be converted to the coordinate type, giving absolute coordinates from a basic reference or a zero point (as used for many years in jig borer practice), when an absolute system is to be used. The conventional type of drawing, in which incremental dimensioning is commonly employed, may be satisfactory for an incremental system. Drawings should preferably have decimal dimensions throughout.

CUTTING TOOL EVALUATIONS

The cutting tool engineer—or the process planner, if he exercises this function as well —must select optimum tooling, from the efficiency, cost, and maintenance standpoints, to meet the requirements of automatic tool changers, turret drilling machines, or tool systems as required. It is especially important that cutting speeds and feeds be re-evaluated, to gain maximum benefit from numerical control. This information in turn must be passed on to the programmer or programming section and fully utilized.

Selection of cutting fluids, or other cooling or lubricating agents, where employed, also their methods of application, and all other conditions of machine operation, should be closely examined and re-evaluated as well.

DESIGN FUNCTION

Product design engineering can also assist in making NC production successful by rationalizing product design and designing with numerical control operation in mind. The former is generally taken for granted in any event, but, to change product design radically, simply to suit numerical control, would detract from the flexibility of NC manufacturing. Further, it may not be possible to exercise any control over the design of parts that may be produced for others on a contract basis. Where possible, part design should be changed to favor simple clamping and setting up. Design changes are chiefly in the tooling, as the fixtures or holding devices can usually be much simpler, and drilling jigs are eliminated in most cases.

TOOL DESIGN AND TOOLMAKING

Although fixtures and work clamping methods can usually be relatively simple, this should not be made an inflexible rule. A more complex fixture may be warranted by the nature of the part, its value, and the quantity to be produced.

Universal fixtures, designed for NC operations, should be fully investigated. Subplates, or subtables, with a pattern of dowel-pin holes for locating workpieces, expedite setups for repetitive pieces in point-to-point work. The numerically controlled machine, once installed, may be used itself to produce its own subplates and fixtures.

It is important to avoid obstacles such as high projecting holding clamps, if possible, to save extra programming for clearing such obstructions. Vises with special locating jaws are adequate in many cases. Vises should preferably be power operated; rapid-action clamps, vises or fixtures, should be used whenever possible.

Since fewer toolmakers are required, some of then can be trained as programmers.

Training Programming and Shop Staff

Advance training of programmers and operators is an important function to include with the preparations. Experienced setup men, toolmakers, machinists, and skilled operators having a good knowledge of machining operations and cutting tools as well as basic mathematics, can be readily trained as programmers for machine tools. In other cases, the methods engineer or process planner may carry out this function. Training for programming and for maintenance is available from the machine tool builders and system manufacturers.

The Programming Organization

Programming in its broadest sense involves all departments, and goes back to training also. Organizing for programming is therefore the sum of all training programs, training of shop staff, establishing good liaison between all engineering and production departments, and the additional factors already mentioned. Cooperation is the key here. And those using the NC equipment must have an interest and confidence in it.

Installation

Details of foundations, vibration control, moving of machine into plant, and other factors of installation should be established in advance in cooperation with the supplier. Power and air supplies, and other shop facilities, should be checked and provided as required.

Location of NC machines, in relation to others and to the work flow, must necessarily take the individual plant's operations and conditions into account.

Any "debugging" of numerical control equipment is now usually at a minimum, and the initial try-out period is shortened.

Planning the Shop Policy

In addition to the training of the operators—and these can usually be the same ones who operated the conventional machines, or can operate them—other advance preparations should be carried out for the shop itself. These practices will assist in NC production:

1. Use preset tooling as much as possible to save setup and programming time. Tool-

offset adjustments, when provided on a machine, to accommodate varying tool lengths such as of drills, are an alternative, dependent on operator attention.

2. Use automatic work transfer methods and equipment when it will speed up parts or materials flow.

3. Try to improve the machine loading method and the handling of stock around the machines.

4. Improve scheduling, or machine loading, to utilize the flexibility of numerical control to its maximum.

5. Review material handling generally throughout the plant as well as in the affected department.

6. Expedite fully and follow through the revisions or changes in the process or production flow as may have been made through the re-evaluations.

7. Correlate production scheduling more closely with the revised inventory requirements arising from NC manufacturing practice.

ESTABLISH A REGULAR MAINTENANCE PROGRAM

A good preventive maintenance program, including mechanical hydraulic, pneumatic, and any other elements, as well as electrical and electronic equipment, should be developed in conjunction with the machine tool builder and systems supplier. Continual operation of numerically controlled machines requires revisions of usual maintenance and servicing schedules, since prolonged shutdowns cannot be tolerated. This may include daily inspection and testing, such as running through a short test tape, with weekly, monthly and annual maintenance schedules.

Modular construction, such as the use of easily tested and removable printed circuit cards, and the use of diagnostic equipment as can be supplied by the manufacturers, have reduced maintenance problems.

Standardization in the equipment, systems and tooling of a plant, can do much to simplify maintenance and keep costs down.

Reorganize Inspection Procedures

Although less inspection is required in numerically controlled manufacturing, it should be precise and fairly rapid, especially for the checking of first parts in production runs. Speed at this stage cuts machine down time.

Coordinate inspection machines with digital readout of hole positions fit in well with point-to-point operations as the operating principles are similar. Other equipment for NC part inspection is available, as is the more advanced tape controlled equipment for complex work. Numerically controlled machines themselves may be used for inspection purposes in some cases.

Inspection equipment that is ample in supply and scope should be provided, and some of it should be used right at the NC machines to assist in setup and for initial checking.

Make Changes in Assembly

As a result of installing numerical control, savings and improvements should be sought in the assembly stages. Smoother assembly is generally possible as a result of the improved and more uniform quality of the numerically controlled production, and a review of methods is indicated in this area.

Reorganize Inventory Control

As numerical control has a marked effect on inventory—which can be reduced to a minimum, due to the flexibility of NC manufacturing and therefore faster replenishment—policies and procedures should be examined and re-assessed in this area as well, to assist in the full utilization of savings available from numerical control operations. Savings in storage space for parts, and in tied-up capital, as the more direct advantages, should be sought and planned.

Selection of Numerical Control Machines and Systems

Planning for investment in numerically controlled equipment demands that attention be paid to the general type of machine and system that is to be selected as well as to the procedures for calculating the return on investment and related factors. Selection of *machine* type, as distinct from system type, is largely influenced by the degree of automation required or justified. Management criteria in such selection are given in Table 8. The general types of machines are not given in the order of their importance in the table, as the order will vary with the individual plant or company.

TABLE 8

MANAGEMENT CRITERIA IN SELECTION OF NUMERICALLY CONTROLLED MACHINES

GENERAL TYPE OF MACHINE	REMARKS
1. Machining or Production Centers with Automatic Tool Changers	For medium to medium-high volume production; capable of performing a large variety of operations.
2. Machines Built for Numerical Control from the Ground Up, for Specific Operations or a Family of Operations	Built for more continuous and higher production than conventional counterparts. Lathes, and turret-type drilling, milling and boring machines, are examples.
3. Manual Machining Centers—with Manual Tool Changing	For intermediate production requirements and variety, small and medium job lots.
4. General Purpose, Numerically Controlled Machines with Alternative Methods of Operation	NC machine tools or other production machinery corresponding to conventional machines, with several modes of operation possible.
5. Numerically Controlled Automatics for Production, also with Alternative Modes of Operation	Examples of such machines are single spindle automatic bar and chucking machines, automatic turret lathes, automatic tool-changing machines and turret drills, or equivalent types, production milling machines, etc.
6. Retrofitted Machines	Not a separate class of machine, but numerical control, such as an NC positioning table, is added to an existing conventional machine.

To Retrofit or Not—Whether to retrofit an existing machine tool with numerical control or not requires careful consideration, and the machine tool builder making comparable equipment should be consulted, especially if he supplies systems as well. Costs, and production results from the two alternative investments must be compared. Machine tools must be in good condition for retrofitting and any necessary rebuilding estimated. Retrofitting should not be rejected out of hand; successful installations of this type have been made and continue in production.

In retrofitting, the operational accuracy expected must be given prime requirements—the machine, even if rebuilt, may not meet the requirements. Also, a new NC machine may have additional features, aside from the numerical control system, which may not be found on the older or retrofitted one. In general, positioning control is more practical for the application of retrofit than is continuous-path control, although the latter is also being used for retrofitting. Usually, the precision requirements are higher for continuous-path than for positioning control, as far as the machine tool itself is concerned, with the possible exception of jig borers.

TECHNICAL CRITERIA IN SELECTION OF NUMERICAL CONTROL SYSTEMS

Table 9 is a review of the main technical considerations in selecting NC systems; only characteristics of absolute and incremental systems will be elaborated upon in the following paragraphs.

TABLE 9

GENERAL TECHNICAL CRITERIA IN SELECTION OF NC SYSTEMS

CRITERIA IN SELECTION	REMARKS
1. Type of Numerical Control as to Main Function	Selection among main system types: positioning or point-to-point control, contouring or continuous-path control, positioning control with rate control (for straight-line cuts), combined positioning and contouring control. Also, selection as to number of axes.
2. Absolute or Incremental Basis of Control	In an absolute system, all measurements are taken from a basic reference point; in an incremental system, the measurements are taken from one positioning point to the next.
3. Analog or Digital System	In analog positioning or movement, the motion of a machine slide is basically continuous, and slide position is analogous to voltage, for example. In a digital system, motions are in individual, discrete (digital) steps (as by means of pulses), even if these are very small. In most systems, there is overlapping of the two principles.
4. Type of Input	Data input into system: punched tape, magnetic tape, manual numerical input by dialing-in method, punched cards.
5. Type of Programming Facilities	These depend largely on the form of input and type of system. The choice may be between a perforating typewriter for punched tape preparation and computer-assisted programming.
6. Other Technical Features and Details of a Control System	Operational features must suit the general type of work to be performed. Some features such as dial input, may be optional (see also Table 10).

Absolute and Incremental Systems—Both types of systems are effectively used. With the absolute system, "synchronization" cannot be lost. It is possible to stop the machining or operation at any point, and resume it at any point in the program, or to return to any selected position or the reference point, because all measurements are taken from the latter.

For absolute systems it is preferable to use drawings with absolute or base line dimensioning, in which the coordinates are calculated or are given from a zero reference point, rather than being incremental from one point to the next on the respective axis.

With an absolute system, changes can be made readily in the program and some dimensions deleted, without recalculating all of the intervening dimensions. And, as noted, the program can be started and stopped at any time; and if a machining operation, for example, is interrupted due to tool trouble or power failure, the operator can generally "pick up" his position more readily with the absolute system than with the incremental one. In the latter case, he may need to return the tool or workpiece to the original or starting position.

In the incremental approach the system measures the positions from the preceding point in each case; programming is likewise on an incremental basis. If a programming error is made in one increment for a position, it is transmitted to all the other positions. The conventional incremental type of drawing can be used for incremental programming. With either the incremental or absolute type of drawing, the data can be abstracted and tabulated from the drawing, for use with whatever type of system is involved.

The possible accumulation of errors, sometimes regarded as a drawback to incremental programming, is being surmounted in the design of such systems, or at least largely prevented. Reduced programming time, and the ability to use conventionally prepared drawings, instead of the absolute type, are some of the advantages of incremental systems.

Additional Choices in Systems—An example of a system that does not fall directly into the usual system classifications, except as to number of axes and some other standard features, is the Sperry UMAC-5 system produced by Sperry Gyroscope Company of Canada, Ltd. This is a solid-state, three-axis position system (optionally up to five axes, one of which can be a rotary application) which is intended to provide special flexibility in adapting it to various machines at the time the installations are made, without making extensive physical changes in the system.

A built-in digital computer has a magnetic memory drum (capacity, 368,640 bits of information, although normal use of the system requires only some 120,000—200,000 bits), operating in conjunction with solid-state logic or computing circuitry. The memory system of the computer stores "canned" operational cycles (called up by tape, but not programmed in detail on the tape); it also provides temporary storage for tape-programmed positioning and other commands, as well as for certain data added as manual digital input. The memory also accommodates up to 32 Z-axis "zero offsets" (tool offsets, or tool-length compensation), and optionally offsets up to 99 tools.

SELECTING OPERATIONAL FEATURES OF SYSTEMS

Some operating features are standard, others are optional with the same system. The main ones are given in Table 10. Additional features may have to be considered in making a selection among several makes of systems. The choices depend on operating requirements, the conveniences that are sought, and the general nature of the work. Optional features may be available at extra cost.

TABLE 10

SELECTION OF OPERATIONAL FEATURES

SYSTEM FEATURE	FUNCTION AND REMARKS
Zero Shift or Zero Offset	Ability to shift or offset the zero position or reference point(s) of the machine; facilitates setting up (in aligning zero of workpiece with zero of table). With full range or full scale zero shift, the zero can be shifted within the full range of a machine table, for example.
Sequence Number Readout	Displays the number of the sequence or operation that the machine and system are carrying out; facilitates following the manuscript, and permits location of any particular sequence, as programmed, to allow its repetition under manual data input.

Continued—Table 10

Selection of Operational Features

SYSTEM FEATURE	FUNCTION AND REMARKS
Manual Digital Input	Manual introduction of position command data (as per decade switches), in addition to tape input. (Alternative manual input for all commands and functions, with some systems.)
Position Display or Digital Readout	Indicates either the programmed or attained position, for one or more axes.
Feed Rate Override	Provides for manual adjustment or change of programmed feed rate to compensate for such factors as varying material hardness and characteristics of cutter.
Automatic Control of Acceleration and Deceleration	Obviates necessity of programming acceleration and deceleration, which are under automatic control instead (with possible minor exceptions).
Cutter Diameter Compensation	Provides automatic compensation if a cutter of slightly larger or smaller diameter than programmed is used when contouring; range may be $\pm$ 0.999 in., for example.
"Manual" Controls for Each Axis	Positioning may be accomplished manually through the servos, saving setup times and checking; may be accomplished through handwheels at the operating console, or through pushbuttons or other means.
Mirror Image Feature	Produces a mirror image from the same tape as used for normal work.
Operator Warning Signals	Lights may show the operator when to change tools in positioning work, or when a cycle is completed.
Tool Length Compensation	Provides for automatic compensation of varying tool lengths in point-to-point positioning, without programming or presetting.
Optional Stop	Permits stopping or interrupting of machine cycle by operator, in contouring, without losing the position or accuracy.

Elements of Numerical Control Systems

The basic principles and elements of numerical control systems were described briefly in earlier chapters, and further details are given here.

FUNCTIONING OF SYSTEM

When the machine control unit, upon instruction from its tape reader, sends out positioning command signals or electrical impulses to the drive unit or servo mechanism, this positions the required machine slide or element. Movement of the slide causes feedback signals to be generated, which are compared with the command signals at the machine control unit. When the desired position has been reached, the command and feedback signals are equal, and no further positioning signals are sent out. The slide will then remain stationary.

The preceding applies to positioning control, but the action is similar with contouring or continuous-path control, where it is a rapid and continuous one. Some systems position without a feedback circuit.

The dimensions of workpieces or parts are of digital nature, and numerical information is digital information. The normal movement of a machine slide however, or the rotation of a leadscrew, are continuous and analog in nature. Digital input must therefore be changed to the analog type somewhere in the system, and the same applies to the action of the feedback part of the system. An alternative is a straight digital system in which the required analog motion is broken down into steps or pulses. When punched tape is used—in whatever type of system—the input is necessarily digital. Hence there is much overlapping of digital and analog operation within a system. Digital signals involve two states—usually these are "on" and "off," although, for example, they can be of opposite voltages instead. Within a control system, digital information is usually associated with counting (as of pulses), whereas analog information calls for comparison of the signal's characteristic with some standard, such as a reference voltage, and voltage may be related to distance.

Voltage signals may be used to make the distance moved proportional to any one of amplitude, phase, or frequency. Other or analog voltage pulse signals can be used as being proportional to distance in magnitude—as to width or height of the individual pulses.

In the Cincinnati Acramatic Thousand series of numerical control systems, for example, the data are handled internally in absolute analog ratio form, being converted internally into analog form using voltage ratio analogs instead of pure voltage amplitude analogs. In this and related Cincinnati systems, the voltage ratio analog values are accurately obtained from precision toroidal transformers (a specific number of turns provides the ratio or percentage of a reference voltage which is imposed across the system).

TAPE READERS AND READING SPEEDS

Tape readers—electromechanical, photoelectric, optical, magnetic, or pneumatic—may have tape reading speeds of 60 to 1,200 characters per second, or still wider ranges, depending on the requirements of the system and type of tape reader. Photoelectric tape readers are generally used where relatively high reading speeds are required.

TRANSDUCERS AND FEEDBACK SYSTEMS

Basically, a transducer is a device which converts one form of energy into another—for example, machine motion into relative electrical signals.

Various types of transducers are used as the position-measuring elements in feedback systems; the synchro, one of the most common, will be dealt with later in this chapter; it can be rotary or linear. Potentiometers in feedback control are described in Chapter 13 (in connection with the Seneca Falls automatic lathe). Rotary synchros, also called resolvers (although the two are not necessarily quite the same), may be rotated by the movement of a leadscrew or a rack and pinion, together with suitable gearing or other arrangement, while the linear synchro has its elements attached to stationary and sliding machine elements.

Analog transducers include synchros, potentiometers, and similar devices. Digital transducers include such examples as pulse generators, encoders, and commutators. Encoders, basically, change analog information to the digital type. All transducers may be divided into two classes—rotary and linear.

The transducers or feedback elements of a feedback system are also referred to as the measuring elements or measuring system, in that positions are continually being measured and their values fed back to the machine control unit. (Not all feedback units are true transducers, however.)

Optical diffraction gratings, as used in systems by Ferranti Ltd., operate in conjunction with a photoelectric cell (or phototransistor) arrangement to continuously measure machine table or slide position, by inititating electrical impulses for feedback control of the servo motors which in turn produce the table or slide movements.

SERVOMECHANISMS, SERVO DRIVES

Servomechanisms are designed to fit the system characteristics as well as the machine tool, especially as to the manner in which the machine slides are to be driven. Electric or hydraulic servo motors (servo drives) may be used, with suitable gearing as may be required. Hydraulic cylinders may be used instead, with electrohydraulic valve control; d-c motors may employ any one of several types of power supplies.

ELEMENTS AND OPERATION OF A REPRESENTATIVE NC SYSTEM

Figure 10–1 is a functional block diagram of a positioning system, as produced by the Allen-Bradley Company.[1]

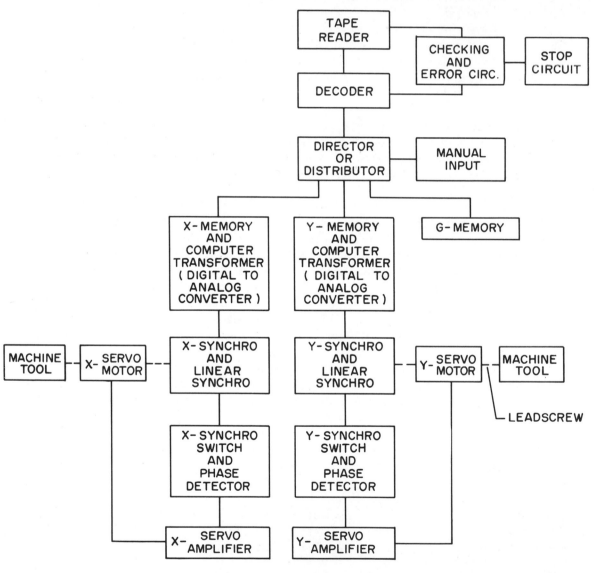

Figure 10–1. Functional block diagram of a numerical positioning control. (Allen-Bradley Company.)

[1] *Theory of Operation, Allen-Bradley Bulletin 1050, Numerical Positioning Controllers* (Milwaukee: Allen-Bradley Company, 1963).

Information input to the system is by means of 1 in. wide, 8-track punched tape coded according to EIA (Electronic Industries Association) standards. (Code details are given in the next chapter.) While a positioning movement is in operation, the system can store the immediately following commands as given on the tape; this makes it unnecessary for the machine to wait for command information for the next positioning movement. The system can be arranged to provide feed rate control.

Functioning of the system is based on a position-difference voltage or position-difference signal, sometimes termed "error voltage" or "error signal." The system uses modular construction, and all electronic circuits are transistorized; it employs reed relays with sealed-in glass contacts. The main elements of the system are: the machine numerical positioning controller (or machine control unit); the machine motion measuring units (feedback units); and the electric motor drives, employing silicon controlled rectifiers (SCR's), replacing the former direct current motors with reversing thyratron drives. (Thyratron—basically, an electron-tube rectifier and switch.)

The Tape Reader—Included in Figure 10–1, the tape reader "reads" the punched tape and sends an output to the decoder. This output is in the form of open and closed circuits, depending on whether or not holes are punched in the tape; there is a set of switches for each row of holes. The tape reader includes a parity checking circuit to help minimize error; tape punched according to the EIA standard must have an odd number of holes in each transverse row of holes ("odd parity"); if an even-numbered row is present, this is detected in the tape reader and the machine is stopped. The transverse rows of holes in the tape are read one at a time, with the tape stopped. Additional contacts of the motorized tape reader carry out further functions, and further error-preventing circuits are included in the reader.

Decoder—The function of the decoder is to interpret the state of switches in the tape reader, as indicated by the presence or absence of holes in the tape. The decoder energizes a single output which corresponds with the character that has been read (a character can be a letter of the alphabet; any integral number from 1 to 9, also zero; a mathematical symbol; or a sign, all as represented by the code holes). The code system used on the tape is of binary coded decimal (BCD) form (explained in the next chapter). Numerical characters need not be decoded, and they proceed through the decoder unchanged.

The tape code employs a "word address" system, which means that a letter or alphabetical character representing the "address" or destination of the command signal must precede the numeric characters representing the position. (If the code letter in this case were replaced by a numeric character, the system would stop.)

Director and Stores—The director or distributor, which can be regarded as the machine control unit, accepts the output from the decoder. The relays which constitute the director are energized when standard non-numeric characters are read. They are "address" relays which energize circuits so as to direct the information from the tape reader to the proper memory or store; for example, the relay for the X address (relative to the X axis of the positioning system), directs the numerical information into the X-axis store, and the Y-address relay directs numerical information to the Y-dimension store or storage. The G-address relay (also in Figure 10–1) directs information to a series of relays that, for example, establish the spindle operating sequence. Additional director relays cause the control system to carry out various commands.

The storage (memory) relay coils for the digits for each axis are energized by D.C. voltage electrical signals emanating from the tape reader and director or, alternatively, by the use of rotary decade switches in the operator's console. These rotary switches are used for dial (manual) numerical input of dimensional or positioning information. (See also last paragraph of this section, concerning reed switches and memory.)

The address-code command signals assure that the appropriate memory relays are energized to store the command information—for machine positioning, or for auxiliary functions such as drilling and tapping cycles. The numbers are stored and locked in their respective memory relays—which belong to the logic circuitry, in this computer-type operation. After the positioning has been carried out, the relays hold in or "remember" the position until such times as they are intentionally dropped to accept new information for positioning.

Synchros for Feedback—For its feedback units, this Allen-Bradley system employs synchros. (Synchro—basically an electromagnetic device, similar to an alternating current motor, which produces a voltage or changes electrical output relative to the angular or rotary position of its rotor.)

A synchro, also called a resolver, is an important form of transducer used in NC systems, and warrants a detailed description. A synchro changes electrical output relative to the angular position of its rotor; therefore, it can also be regarded in another sense as a device which converts an angle into a corresponding analog voltage.

The rotor shaft of the synchro in the Allen-Bradley system, shown diagrammatically in Figure 10–2, is geared to the machine, generally through the leadscrew driving a machine slide. The rotor then assumes an angle as determined by the machine or slide position. The output voltages of the rotor therefore depend on the positions of the moving machine element and the value or magnitude of the sine and cosine voltages, as will be explained.

Referring again to Figure 10–2, the two electrical inputs to the stator of the synchro consist of alternating-current voltages of 2,010 c.p.s. (cycles per sec.); one of the inputs has an amplitude proportional to the sine of the final position angle of the synchro, and the other electrical input to the stator has an amplitude which is proportional to the cosine of the angle. A third input is the angle of the rotor. Two outputs from the rotor vary in magnitude with the rotor angle and the value or magnitude of the sine and cosine voltages. The third input to the synchros is an interpolating voltage inserted into the rotor winding.

Further, the action of the synchros is as follows: applying a voltage which is proportional in amplitude to the sine of an angle to one of the stator windings of the synchro, and a voltage which is proportional to the cosine of the angle to the second stator winding, will result in the output from the rotor windings being zero when the rotor is turned to the corresponding angle. (Synchros with two rotor windings produce outputs which are 90 degrees out of phase with each other in relation to the rotor-position angle; if the output from one winding is zero, the output of the second winding will therefore be the maximum.) It must be noted that intermediate angles of rotor voltages are proportional to the sine of the angle, basically, and in this application of synchros to the Allen-Bradley system.

When a leadscrew drive is employed, four rotary synchros may be geared to the leadscrew, with a 10 to 1 ratio between each. The synchro having the highest gear ratio makes one revolution per inch of travel of the machine table or slide. The synchro with the next highest ratio is geared to make one revolution for every 10 in. of travel or motion; the next or third synchro is geared to turn through one revolution in each 100 in. of travel, and the fourth synchro makes one revolution for 1,000 in. of travel or motion. An additional linear synchro, as will be described further, has a period of 0.1 in. Rotary synchros may be used with a rack and pinion arrangement, instead of with a leadscrew.

Another arrangement can have 0.1 in. of travel or machine motion per revolution of the first synchro, 1 in. per revolution for the second synchro, 10 in. per revolution for the third, and so on. In this Allen-Bradley numerical control system, three or four rotary synchros and usually a linear synchro, are employed for the feedback system. The synchro

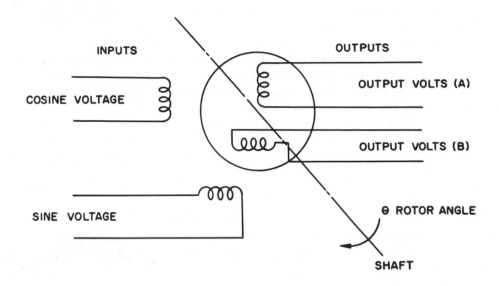

Figures 10–2 & 10–3. At top: A rotary synchro, also called resolver, as used for feedback on the Allen-Bradley positioning system. (Allen-Bradley Company.) At bottom: A linear synchro used for position measuring in the feedback system. (Allen-Bradley Company.)

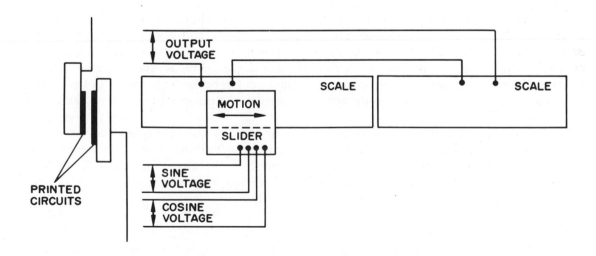

gear ratio has since been changed to 100:1 instead of the former 10:1, and only a single rotor winding is employed.

Linear Synchros—A linear synchro carries out the same function as the rotary type, except that "sliding" motions are involved instead. The "scales" of the linear synchro are attached to the stationary machine member, and the "slider" to the travelling member, although this arrangement can be reversed. The linear synchro has one slider and one or more scales. (The linear synchro in this case is an Inductosyn unit, by Farrand Controls, Inc.) It must be emphasized, however, that there is no sliding action in the usual sense, since there is a small air gap between scale and slider.

The slider is a metal plate of about 3 × 5 in., having a printed circuit which is equivalent to the stator windings of the rotary synchros. The scale is a metal plate, about 10 × 2 in., also with a printed circuit, but which is equivalent to the rotor windings of the rotary synchros. To increase the length as required, several scales may be placed end to end.

The linear synchro carries out the same task as the rotary synchros, namely, to produce an output voltage having a magnitude which depends upon the machine (or slide) position and the input voltages. A linear synchro is shown in the diagram of Figure 10–3. This unit has a period of 0.1 in.

Digital to Analog Converter—The numbers which are stored in the memory relays, and which are digital in nature, are converted to analog form in the digital-to-analog converter (see Figure 10–1 again), a "computer" transformer, so that the command can be compared with the feedback signal. The circuitry produces a position-difference signal for the servo drive if the two signals disagree.

Synchro Switch—The synchro switch operates in conjunction with the synchros, each of which puts out its own position-difference voltage. The latter is applied to the synchro switch, which is of static type. The switch forms a single output "error voltage" which finally actuates the servo control, so that the servo drive brings the machine table or slide to the programmed position. (The synchro switch feeds into a discriminator and then into the servo drive; fundamentally, discriminators, of which there are various types, select signals according to certain current characteristics—such as frequency, amplitude, or phase—or, convert characteristics. In this instance, the synchro switch and discriminator convert the 2,010 c.p.s. position-difference voltages from the synchros into direct-current voltages which can be accepted by the drives. As this point is reached, the synchros stop their own output.)

The error voltage, or more correctly, position-difference voltage, indicates the desired distance and direction of motion through its amplitude and phase relationship to a reference voltage.

The Allen-Bradley system, as briefly described, is of absolute type. Zero offset and various additional features are provided. Changes in the system have involved, among other elements, the tape reader, decoder, and the memory, with information stored in a matrix switch built of reed switches. The foregoing description, however, serves to explain basic system action.

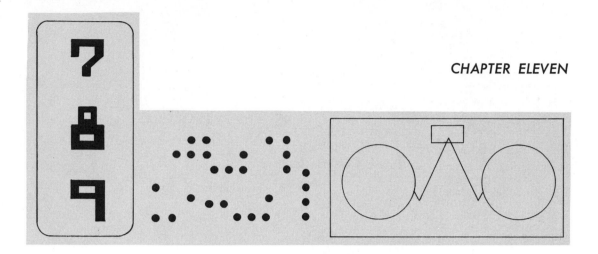

BASIC POINTS
IN PROGRAMMING

THE FLOW OF COMMAND INFORMATION FROM THE PUNCHED TAPE TO THE MACHINE, AFTER PASSING THROUGH THE TAPE READER AND MACHINE CONTROL UNIT, IS INDICATED IN FIGURE 11–1. (SEE ALSO SYSTEM BLOCK DIAGRAMS OF CHAPTERS 3 AND 10.)

THE MACHINE IS A VERTICAL SPINDLE DRILLING, BORING, AND STRAIGHT-CUT MILLING MACHINE, WITH A TWO-AXIS POSITIONING SYSTEM (X AND Y AXES). THE TAPE COMMANDS (ALSO KNOWN AS COMMAND "WORDS") ARE SHOWN IN ABBREVIATED FORM; THE TAPE CODES (VALUES OF PUNCHED HOLES, THEIR LOCATIONS, SEQUENCE, AND SO ON) ARE EXPLAINED LATER IN THIS CHAPTER.

THE TABLE AND SADDLE ARE MOVED AT 90 DEGREES TO EACH OTHER ON THEIR RESPECTIVE SLIDES, FOR RECTANGULAR COORDINATE POSITIONING OF THE WORKPIECE RELATIVE TO THE TOOL, WHICH IN THIS CASE, IS A DRILL.

119

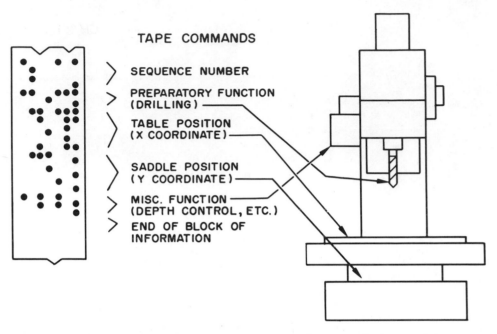

Figure 11–1. Principle of information flow from punched tape (via tape reader and machine control unit) to machine slides or elements.

Location of Reference Zero—The reference zero for the X and Y coordinates may be located at the front left-hand corner of the machine table, for example, or at some other or central point. If a third or Z axis is used, as for a vertical spindle, its zero or reference point may be so many inches above the table surface, and as determined by the system design. The method selected for the location of the reference zero depends on the system and/or drawing in use. When full-range zero shift is provided, the zero point can be shifted as desired.

The Four Coordinate Areas or Quadrants

When locating the reference zero at the center of a table or drawing, four coordinate areas or quadrants are employed, as in Figure 11–2. The X and Y axes intersect each other at the center, the origin or reference zero. Positions in the various quadrants, as in graph practice, have the usual plus or minus values according to the location of the quadrant.

On the part drawing the dimensions in each of the four quadrants thus formed may be prefaced with plus or minus signs, according to their quadrant positions.

The system may be designed to operate in all four quadrants. This involves plus and minus programming, in which the coordinate dimension with its X or Y code is likewise prefixed with a plus or minus sign (although plus signs may be omitted) to indicate quadrant location. The quadrants, as shown and described, are in one plane.

If a workpiece has holes located on and dimensioned according to a pitch circle and its centre (four-quadrant location), it is still possible to use single-quadrant programming, if necessary, by adjusting the coordinate dimensions relative to a zero point lying outside the pitch circle. The plus and minus signs may then be omitted.

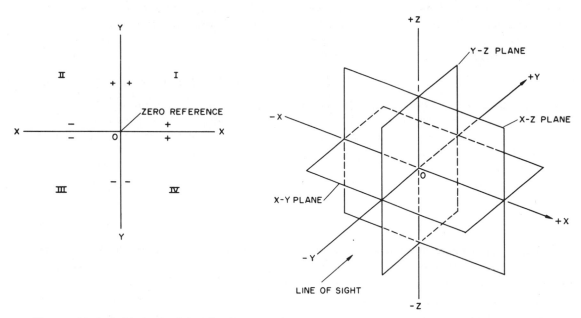

Figures 11–2 & 11–3. At left: The four quadrants or coordinate areas for coordinate dimension-ing and programming. At right: The three axes and coordinates of three planes, or Cartesian coordinates.

In an absolute system and in absolute programming, all distances are calculated from the zero point. In incremental programming, each new position is calculated from the immediately preceding one.

CARTESIAN COORDINATES

The three axes and coordinates of three planes, or Cartesian coordinates, are shown in Figure 11–3, which also indicates the positive and negative quadrants on the axes. Angular rotation may also be involved around the X, Y and Z axes.

CONTINUOUS-PATH PROGRAMMING

Contour or continuous-path programming, as for positioning, can be of the manual or the computer-assisted type.

Curves or circle arcs can be resolved into a series of very short, straight lines or chords, which, in total, produce a smooth curve, within tolerances, along the part that is contour machined. This is *linear interpolation* of a circle arc. If performed by the system itself, it is internal linear interpolation. External interpolation can be manual or computer-assisted.

In *circular interpolation*, the detailed computing is generally performed within the system itself (internal interpolation). Simple specification codes, such as giving the two distances to the arc center from the start of the arc as X and Y coordinates, also the direction code and end point of the arc, are punched into the tape. (Examples follow in Chapter 12.)

Parabolic interpolation utilizes parabolic portions or spans to produce curves by automatic interpolation within the system. The spans are also blended automatically.

Some systems can operate according to any one of these three forms of interpolation which are computed and performed automatically with a minimum of programmed information input. If the contours to be machined are not complex, the basic calculations can be performed on a desk calculator. For complex work, computer routines should be employed.

Linear interpolation is usually a standard feature, when available with a system, while circular and parabolic interpolation may be optional.

ACCELERATION AND DECELERATION

Various numerical control systems automatically control acceleration and deceleration, so that these need not be programmed separately. Others require final positioning to take place at a slower rate for a short distance; also, if hole locations are close, in positioning operations a slower positioning rate may have to be programmed, depending on the individual system.

The different types of information that must be placed on the tape will first be explained briefly at this point.

POSITIONING OR DIMENSIONAL INFORMATION

This is coordinate information, tape commands for movements on the X, Y, or Z axes, as may be required. For example, the command X12312 may call for the table to move 12.312 in. from the zero point along the X axis. Using a letter to indicate the "address" or destination of the command in this way is known as the "word address tape format"; there are other formats, as will be shown.

Plus and minus signs used with coordinate dimensions in continuous-path programming indicate directions from the zero reference or starting point.

FUNCTIONAL INFORMATION

The "miscellaneous function" codes, also known as the "m" codes, are preceded by the letter m (or M).

The first 10 functions and their codes, as commonly used, conforming to EIA (Electronic Industries Association) standards, are as follows:

m00	Program Stop	m05	Spindle Off
m01	Optional Stop	M06	Tool Change
m02	End of Program	m07	Unassigned
m03	Spindle Clockwise	m08	Coolant On
m04	Spindle Counterclockwise	m09	Coolant Off

A programmed stop (m00) results in automatic stopping of the machine for a manual tool change or other operation. An optional stop may be overridden by the operator; it is intended for inspection or checking purposes, and so on.

The code digits following the letter m may also be chosen to suit the user's particular requirements.

ADDITIONAL DATA AND SEQUENCE OF DATA ON TAPE

A "block" of information on a punched tape contains all the data necessary to carry out one positioning movement or one operation.

The main word address codes and sequence of placing them on the punched tape, using EIA standard or associated codes, can be as follows, depending on the individual system:

1. *Block Number:* This is also known as sequence number or operation number; the code designation is N or n followed by three digits, e.g., n001 for the first block, and n002 for the second block, and so on.

2. *Preparatory Functions:* These refer to general operations or functions, and the code letter,

again in the word address system, is *g*. For example, a g5 command may indicate "spindle to move to location in a point-to-point manner with spindle up; then drill or bore."

In contouring, some examples of basic preparatory commands and codes (in this case, as applied to General Electric Mark Century contouring control) are:

g01   *Straight lines and slopes, using linear interpolation*
g02   *Clockwise arcs, using circular interpolation*
g03   *Counterclockwise arcs, with circular interpolation*
g04   *Programmed dwell (for example, 0 to 100 sec.)*

3. *X Dimension or Coordinate:* (See preceding paragraph "Positioning or Dimensional Information.")

4. *Feed Function:* The feed function has the code *f*, for each movement (in programming for continuous-path, as well as for straight-cut milling with point-to-point systems).

The EIA standard feed rate code, which follows here in detail, consists of three digits following the letter or word address *f* or *F*. The second and third digits give the feed rate directly in inches per minute, rounded off to two digits, and the first digit indicates the position of the decimal point by a value which is greater by three numbers (units) than the number of digits to the left of the decimal point.

For example, a feed rate of 63.00 i.p.m. (inches per minute) would be shown as F563, the first digit on the left being the sum of 2 plus 3. A feed of 0.063 i.p.m. would be shown as F263, the first digit being the sum of minus 1 plus 3 (i.e., $-1 +3$). A feed of 0.630 i.p.m. would be F363, the first digit 3 derived from $0 + 3$, and so on, in this feed rate code which has been called the "Magic Three" code.

5. *Tool Function:* A tool number or tool function may be represented by the code letter *t*, with a tool number as assigned on the process planning or operations sheet for point-to-point programming.

6. *Continuous-Path Arc or Contour Data:* In continuous-path programming, the data and codes for arcs or curves may follow at this point (see examples in Chapter 12 for details).

7. *Miscellaneous Functions:* The address code *m*, usually followed by two digits, as explained previously.

8. *End of Block:* The Code EB denotes the end of a block of tape information.

Tape Preparation Equipment

The equipment used for punching tape can range from a relatively simple manual tape punch to computer production of tapes, with computer routines.

AUTOMATIC PERFORATING TYPEWRITER

A widely used machine for preparing punched tape is the Friden Flexowriter equipped with an automatic tape punch. The machine is basically a heavy duty, automatic (electric) writing machine, its keyboard and general form resembling an electric typewriter. When equipped with a tape punch, the machine automatically punches a tape in coded form as the information from a document—such as a program manuscript or the information from it—is being manually typed or keyboarded on this machine. This at the same time produces a printout of the document or program manuscript.

A Flexowriter unit with a tape punch may have a "motorized tape reader" connected to it by electric cable, for verifying the punched tape. There is also a tape reader proper (at the front left of the machine, ahead of the tape punch). Tape which has been punched on the Flexowriter may be duplicated by running it through this tape reader, the Flexowriter and automatic tape punch automatically accomplishing the rest, also producing a duplicate print-out. (Used as an automatic writing machine, the Flexowriter machine can therefore type or print a document, or make quantity copies from a punched tape; this method is distinct from manual keyboard operation.)

MANUAL TAPE PUNCHES

Various manual tape punches have been made available through machine tool or systems manufacturers during the past; some have evolved into more versatile and faster machines, providing the necessary time-saving features.

PRINTED CIRCUIT TAPE PREPARATION UNIT

An example of a specialized unit is the Edlund Printed Circuit Programmer by the Edlund Machinery Company. It is designed for preparing 1 in., eight-channel or eight-track tape directly from printed circuit board art work, for subsequent numerically controlled drilling of printed circuit boards. Essentially, the machine has a movable stylus which is traversed across the grid of the art work, its path controlled by X and Y guide bars. A position is read and punched into the tape, using the correct address letter and the minimum number of digits that may be required. (Edlund Machinery Company has since become the Edlund Division, Monarch Machine Tool Company.)

TAPE PUNCHED WITH FIRST PART OFF MACHINE

An automatic tape punch may be available as optional equipment, as with the Moog Hydra-Point system as made by Moog Inc., Hydra-Point Division; it provides for automatic punching of a control tape as the first part is made on the machine under manual digital input. The subsequent pieces are then run off under tape control.

PUNCHED TAPE FROM COMPUTER

When using computer programming, a punched control tape is obtained from the computer at the same time.

MAGNETIC TAPE FROM COMPUTER

Magnetic tape for control systems requiring it may be obtained through computer programming techniques, or, punched tape may be converted in a computer to magnetic tape for use as the control tape. In other cases, magnetic tape preparation units may be used.

VERIFYING PUNCHED TAPE

Proofreading the data on the printout (typed document) from an automatic tape-punching typewriter against the original program manuscript or sheet (see examples in Chapter 12) is one accepted method to verify punched tape.

Another way, in positioning work, is to verify and prove the tape on the NC machine itself, by lightly spot drilling all hole positions first, under control of the tape. Errors in coordinates, if any, are usually large enough to be detected readily by this method, before any serious damage is done to the workpiece. An alternative—both in positioning and continuous-path work—is to run off a trial part using some easily machined material. Another alternative, as an approximate check, is a "dry" run or simulated run, on the machine.

Another method is to process the control tape through a numerically controlled drafting machine, to plot the coordinates, before running off any actual parts. Several systems have been evolved, in which a drawing of the part is produced, which is then compared with the original part print, the specifications, or the programmed data.

Tape may also be checked to a degree by producing two tapes and placing one on top of the other to see if the hole patterns are the same. The tape preparation equipment itself can often be used for verifying the tape that was punched on it—either by facilitating a visual check for comparsion, or otherwise by some automatic means.

To verify tape that has been punched on the Friden Flexowriter, the previously mentioned motorized tape reader can be employed. This model of tape preparation unit also contains a *parity code* checking device which assures that, as in the EIA standard tape coding system, every transverse row of punched holes in the tape will contain an odd number instead of an even number of holes. If an *odd parity* hole is missing, this arrangement will detect it. Verification of computer prepared tape may be confined to the "proveout" of the entire program and tooling, during machining of the first part with that tape.

The original tape is generally kept as a master and stored, and the second or duplicate tape goes to the machine on the production floor.

Computer Programming Routines

Although computer assisted programming was originally intended to supplant complex continuous-path calculations and manual programming, various computer routines are now available to accommodate a wide variety of numerical control applications. They can save time even for the less complicated positioning programs, and can be especially useful also when a great many short runs of different types are involved, or when much prototype work is to be done, and programming is required at very short notice.

With computer programming, particularly for contouring, it is usually only necessary to describe the part in abbreviated word code or computer language.

THE APT SYSTEM

This system (APT—Automatic Programming for Tools, or Automatically Programmed Tools) is available to participating companies or organizations from IIT Research Institute, Technology Center (Chicago, Ill.). The APT computer programming system is used for both contouring and point-to-point applications, to perform detailed programming and provide control tapes.

Letters or abbreviated English words are employed in computer-language code to describe the required operations; they are then translated into numerical signals by the computer. Some examples of the English-like APT language follow:

SPINDL/2400	Turn on spindle; set at 2,400 r.p.m.
COOLNT/FLOOD	Turn on coolant; use flood setting.
PT1 = POINT/4,5	Define a reference point, PT1, as the point with co-ordinates (4,5).
GO LFT/(LINE/2,4,1,3), PAST, BASE	Go left along the line joining the points (2,4,) and (1,3) past the line BASE.

Such prepared instructions may be entered on an APT part program symbolic sheet, a standard type of form. Usually these instructions are prepared from a part print, but they may also be prepared from a mathematical description of the part to be manufactured. The APT language contains over 250 word-symbols which serve to give instructions to a computer.

Changes in various computer routines continue to be made as this technology progresses.

AUTOPROMT AND OTHER IBM SYSTEMS

Several methods of computer assisted programming are available through International Business Machines Corporation, Data Systems Division (Poughkeepsie, N. Y.). AUTO-PROMT, which stands for Automatic Programming of Machine Tools, as in the previous system example, does not require a detailed knowledge of computer programming, and uses descriptive phrases which are readily understood by processing or programming personnel.

The AUTOPROMT system, it should be added, is designed to accommodate any general three-dimensional surface in its computer programming for automatic calculation of tool travel paths. For plants which do not possess computers, processing services for this system are made available through IBM data centers.

Post process routines, which are secondary or follow-up computer programs, fill in numerous details to adapt the initially computer-programmed data to specific machine tools, as to available speeds, feeds, and so on.

AUTOPROPS, or Automatic Programming for Positioning Systems, was developed jointly by IBM and Pratt & Whitney Company, Incorporated. With this system, simple numerical statements are used by the programmer to specify the hole centers in a part. The computer, in processing these statements, produces punched tape to control the positioning functions of the machine tool.

Another IBM computer programming system is the AUTOSPOT program (Automatic System for Positioning Tools) which the company developed for use with a card-oriented data processing system, and intended for both positioning and continuous-path programming.

COMPUTER ROUTINES BY BUILDERS AND SYSTEMS MANUFACTURERS

Computer routines have been devised by major machine tool builders and the makers of numerical control systems. SNAP (for Simplified Numerical Automatic Programmer) was developed by Brown & Sharpe Manufacturing Company, in cooperation with International Business Machines Corporation.

CINAP (Cincinnati Numerical Automatic Programming), was developed by The Cincinnati Milling Machine Co., for continuous-path programming. CINTAP is a later development of the company.

SPLIT (from Sundstrand Processing Language Internally Translated), is another computer routine for programming two-axis contouring, by Sundstrand Machine Tool.

Various additional systems, all designed to speed up and simplify programming, have been and are being developed.

The GECENT postprocessor, developed by the General Electric Company for its Mark Century numerical controls, was designed for use with the APT III computer program system. The latter system provides instructions for a general purpose computer to calculate the coordinate points which the cutter is intended to follow.

These computer routines, as well as additional ones, are usually available as a programming service from the quoted sources, from most of the major machine tool makers, and systems manufacturers. Using such services makes it unnecessary to install a general purpose computer, or to rent one, and only the initial programming may need to be done in the plant. Word descriptions of the part to be produced can be readily transmitted to such computing centers by telephone or any one of the usual communication methods, depending also on the type of computer routine employed.

In continuous-path programming, when using some computer routines, it is only necessary to calculate the change points, or blend points, along curves or contours. In the APT programming system, for example, even these calculations may be omitted.

Standard Tape Codes and Coding Procedures

The eight tracks of the EIA standard, 1 in. wide punched tape, provide for eight holes in any one transverse row, but only up to 7 holes are normally used, to allow application of the parity check. There is an additional track of smaller holes, for the sprocket drive.

TAPE MATERIALS AND SPECIFICATIONS

Materials used for punched tape include: strong paper, oiled or paraffin coated, for positioning control; high strength plastic, such as Mylar, which may be a Mylar-laminated paper tape, or a clear Mylar plastic tape; and other materials, such as special vulcanized fiber, depending also on type of tape reader and desired life of tape. The latter may range from about 100–250 cycles or runs through the reader, for oiled or paraffin-coated paper tape, to some 10,000 cycles for Mylar plastic tape.

Paraffin coated tape and Mylar laminated tape can be readily spliced with ordinary cements, as well as be written on to identify the tape.

Tape Specifications—Dimensional specifications for EIA tape [1] include the following: unpunched tape must have an overall width of 1.000 ± 0.003 in., after specified conditioning; thickness of unpunched tape must be 0.004 ± 0.0003 in., also after specified conditioning involving temperature and humidity; and the tape is to be used for recording six, seven or eight levels of information across the tape.

Further, center lines of holes must be spaced 0.100 in. apart ($\frac{1}{10}$ of an in.), both transversely and longitudinally; code holes in the tape shall be round with a diameter of $0.072 + 0.001$ in $- 0.002$ in.; the feed holes in the tape must be round with a diameter of $0.046 + 0.002$ in. $- 0.001$ in. Some additional specifications must also be met. These physical specifications do not affect the coding as such, but provide standardization and interchangeability.

BCD NUMBER SYSTEM

The binary-coded decimal (BCD) numbering system is most widely used for the numerical data. This system combines elements of both the usual decimal or ten-number system, based on the number 10, and the binary numbering system, which is based on the number 2 (also called the base 2 number system).

BINARY NUMBERS

In the common decimal or ten-number system, the numerals or numbers from 1 to 9 are used, as well as 0 (10 numerals); the digits in a figure, to the left of the decimal point, are (positive) powers of 10: units, tens, hundreds, thousands, and so on.

In the binary system, or the two-number system, which is a numbering or notation system based on the number 2, only two numbers are used—zero (0) and 1 (one). From the right to the left in a binary number, the values for each digit are multiplied by 2, instead of by 10, as compared with the decimal system. For example, the binary numbers 1011 and 111101 have the values of 11 and 61 respectively in the decimal or ten-number system; as shown by the following:

---

[1] *One-Inch Perforated Paper Tape, Standard RS-227* (Washington, D.C.: Electronic Industries Association, 1959).

BINARY NUMBER 1011			BINARY NUMBER 111101		
1st digit from the right	$1 \times 1 =$	1	1st digit from the right	$1 \times 1 =$	1
2nd digit	$2 \times 1 =$	2	2nd digit	$2 \times 0 =$	0
3rd digit	$4 \times 0 =$	0	3rd digit	$4 \times 1 =$	4
4th digit	$8 \times 1 =$	8	4th digit	$8 \times 1 =$	8
		—	5th digit	$16 \times 1 =$	16
		11	6th digit	$32 \times 1 =$	32
					—
					61

The equivalent numbers from 1 to 12 in the decimal and binary numbering systems follow:

DECIMAL NUMBERS	BINARY NUMBERS	DECIMAL NUMBERS	BINARY NUMBERS
0	0	7	111
1	1	8	1000
2	10	9	1001
3	11	10	1010
4	100	11	1011
5	101	12	1100
6	110		

With the decimal system, the individual digits of a figure or number are powers of 10, in the binary system, they are powers of 2. Stated otherwise, in the decimal or ten-number system, figures are expressed in multiples of 1, 10, 100, 1,000, and so on, but in the binary or two-number system, in terms of multiples of 1, 2, 4, 8, 16, 32, 64, 128, etc.

The figure 27, in the decimal system, may be expressed in binary powers as follows:

$$(1 \times 2^4) + (1 \times 2^3) + (0 \times 2^2) + (1 \times 2^1) + (1 \times 2^0)$$

Expressed in binary form, and reading only the identifying digits in the brackets, the decimal figure 27 becomes 11011 in the binary system.

Binary-Decimal Code vs. Straight Decimal Code—Instead of using a straight decimal code on tape—with a track or channel for each number or numeral—for example, employing 10 channels or tracks on the tape to represent the numerals from 0 to 9—the binary-coded decimal system, combining principles of both the decimal and binary number systems, is used. By directly employing only the numbers 1, 2, 4, and 8, it is possible to represent all the numbers from 1 to 9 by using up only four tracks. The remaining numbers 3, 5, 6, 7, and 9 are obtained by addition; for instance, 3 is obtained as $2 + 1$, 5 as $4 + 1$, 7 as $4 + 2 + 1$, etc. These combined numbers of course, use up additional transverse rows of tape, extending its length. (In other words, the numerals from 1 to 9 would take up 9 transverse rows, but use a total of only four tracks, plus another track for the parity code.)

The straight binary code is also used, but the BCD or binary coded decimal system predominates in tape coding. Straight binary numbers lend themselves well to the principle of "on-off" switching, because they employ only two numerals: 1 and 0; however, when using many binary numbers in succession, the repetition of 1 and 0 can become monotonous and may affect the accuracy of calculations more so than with the above number systems and tape codes. (See also binary reference chart of Figure 11–4.)

THE HOLE CODES FOR EIA STANDARD PUNCHED TAPE

Following are descriptions of the codes used for EIA standard 1 in., eight-track or eight-channel punched tape using the binary coded decimal (BCD) system. In addition to the provision for the eight longitudinal tracks (channels or levels) or series of holes, there

CONVERSION RULES
DECIMAL TO BINARY

DIVIDE BY TWO, WHEN REMAINDER
IS EVEN WRITE 0, WHEN THE
REMAINDER IS ODD SUBTRACT
ONE AND WRITE ONE.

EXAMPLE

$327 = 326 + 1$ (LSB)
  $162 + 1$
   $80 + 1$
   $40 + 0$
   $20 + 0$
   $10 + 0$
    $4 + 1$
    $2 + 0$
    $0 + 1$ (MSB)

$= 10100011 1$ (LSB)

CONVERSION RULES
BINARY TO DECIMAL

START WITH MSB, DOUBLE IF
NEXT DIGIT IS ZERO, DOUBLE
AND ADD ONE IF THE NEXT
DIGIT IS A ONE.

EXAMPLE 101101

$1 \times 2 + 0 = 2$
$2 \times 2 + 1 = 5$
$5 \times 2 + 1 = 11$
$11 \times 2 + 0 = 22$
$22 \times 2 + 1 = 45$
$101101 = 45$

POWERS OF "2"

2^0	UNIT (1)
2^1	2
2^2	4
2^3	8
2^4	16
2^5	32
2^6	64
2^7	128
2^8	256
2^9	512
2^{10}	1024
2^{11}	2048
2^{12}	4096
2^{13}	8192
2^{14}	16384
2^{15}	32768
2^{16}	65536
2^{17}	131072
2^{18}	262144
2^{19}	524288
2^{20}	1048567
2^{21}	2097152
2^{22}	4194304
2^{23}	8388608

BIT A "ONE" IN THE
BINARY NUMBERING
SYSTEM
MSB THE MOST
SIGNIFICANT BIT
LSB THE LEAST
SIGNIFICANT BIT

Figure 11–4. Reference chart for binary numbers and number system conversion. (The Bendix Corporation, Industrial Controls Section.)

is the series of smaller sprocket drive holes. The eight-track arrangement of course provides eight hole positions in each transverse row of punched holes, but only up to seven are generally used in the same row, thus conforming to the previously described odd-parity check.

Character: A Unit of Information—The term "character" means any single or individual piece of information that is to be punched into the tape. It can be a numeral or number from 0 to 9; a letter of the alphabet, a punctuation sign, a plus or minus sign, or other symbol. Characters may also include codes which are required in the operation of an automatic perforating typewriter.

The coded information for *only one character* can be placed in any transverse row, and normally, the code for any single character may require from a single hole to seven holes in a transverse row, depending on the character to be represented or coded.

Coding for Numbers—The binary coded decimal system for punching tape employs the numbers 1, 2, 4, and 8, as noted before. These are assigned to track Nos. 1, 2, 3, and 4, respectively (see Figure 11–5). (The sprocket-hole track shown is not assigned a number.) The holes shown in track No. 5 are for the parity check only, and have no numerical value.

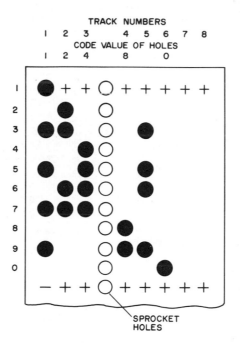

Figure 11–5. Binary-decimal coding for numerals only, on EIA standard 1 in., eight-track or eight-level punched tape. (Holes for the parity check are in track No. 5; they have no numerical value.)

Zero is placed in track No. 6.

The remaining numbers, 3, 5, 6, 7, and 9, are obtained by addition: 3 as 2 + 1, 5 as 4 + 1, 6 as 4 + 2, 7 as 4 + 2 + 1, and 9 as 8 + 1.

Parity Check for Accuracy—When a code results in an even number of holes in a transverse row, an additional hole is punched in track No. 5. All transverse rows therefore must have an odd number of holes in them. This parity check system, also termed odd parity, as used with the binary coded decimal system, improves the reliability to a considerable extent.

The numeral 3, for instance, requires two holes, one in track No. 1 and another in track No. 2; to conform to the parity check, a third hole is therefore punched in track No. 5, which is reserved for that purpose, resulting in three holes for that transverse row.

The tape reader of the numerical control system will not read an even number of holes, unless the tape has been damaged, the automatic tape punching typewriter has functioned improperly, or the tape reader itself is at fault. In any event, if the tape is read by the system, the numerical control system automatically stops, and the machine is prevented from carrying out a false command.

Coding for Letters of Alphabet—The letters from A to R are accommodated in track No. 7 and additionally in Nos. 1 to 6, and the letters S to Z in track No. 6 and with additional holes in track Nos. 1 to 5. The letter A is represented by three holes (see right hand view of Figure 11–6), a hole in each of track Nos. 1, 6 and 7, and the letter E, another example, uses five holes, one in each of track Nos. 1, 3, 5, 6 and 7.

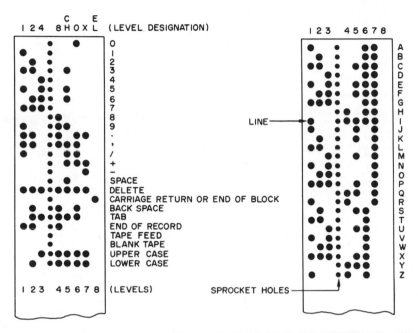

Figure 11–6. The EIA Standard punched tape codes for all numerals, letters, and other instructions for the binary-coded decimal system; tape has 8 levels or tracks. (The Boeing Company (Wichita, Kans.), and American Machine Tool Distributors Association.)

Track or channel No. 7 is sometimes referred to as the "X-codes" channel, but it should be noted that the letter X does not have any part of its code in track No. 7, but that it requires the use of track Nos. 1, 2, 3, 5, and 6. Figure 11–6 gives all commonly used codes. The letters I and O may be omitted, to avoid confusion with the numerals 1 and 0 (zero). As far as the tape code itself is concerned, there can be no confusion between the letter O and the numeral zero, as the latter is placed only in track No. 6.

Shown also in Figure 11–6 are punctuation and plus and minus sign codes, and data relating to both machine operation and operation of an automatic tape-punching typewriter, for example, the "Carriage Return or End of Block" code.

End of Block Code—"Carriage Return or End of Block," designated as EL (End of Line) or more often, EB (End of Block), indicates the end of a block of information. A block can mean all the commands required to carry out a positioning movement, an entire operation, or a similar block of information.

Tab Code—Used in several types of tape formats (see "Standard Tape Formats" following), the Tab code, entered by punching the Tab key on the tape punching typewriter, separates individual commands, such as the X and Y coordinates, and has functions as to be discussed here under formats.

Other Code-Hole Values—The "Tape Feed" code refers to the sprocket drive holes, which occupy a separate track or level between tracks 3 and 4. Only the tape feed or sprocket holes may be punched to start the tape leader. The "Blank Tape" code likewise requires continued punching of sprocket holes only, leaving blank space on the tape, for a purpose such as writing the tape identification. Space for identification, however, may be provided by punching the "Space" code holes.

Codes which are included for operating an automatic tape punching typewriter, such as Space, Delete, Decimal Point, and End of Record, are generally ignored by the NC system. The Tab code may also be ignored, depending on the type of control.

With regard to all codes, it should be noted that the track numbers start on the "narrower" side of the tape relative to the track of sprocket holes.

STANDARD TAPE FORMATS

The term "format" as applied to punched tape, sometimes loosely termed the tape code, refers chiefly to the general arrangement; the sequence in which the coded information is placed on the tape; and the manner of identifying and "addressing" the commands—to make certain that each command is directed to its proper circuit or memory store in the system.

Word Address Format—As described briefly before, this format uses a letter of the alphabet as a "word address" in front of a command to identify it and insure that the system will direct the command signal to its proper circuit. Because of this identification and the design of the system, the sequence of the positioning commands, for example, need not be important, although the X coordinate is usually programmed before the Y coordinate (for instance, X23751, Y18375, in this case representing positioning movements of 23.751 in. and 18.375 in. on the X and Y axes respectively).

The sequence number, the miscellaneous and preparatory or auxiliary functions, likewise have their own word addresses, as explained earlier in this chapter. All of the commands in a block are listed and programmed in a standard sequence, depending on system type (see programming examples in Chapter 12).

Tab Sequential Format—This format requires no word addresses for the individual commands. The Tab code (holes in track Nos. 2, 3, 4, 5, and 6 in a transverse row) is punched to precede each command; in a typical Tab sequential program, the position of a Tab code in the sequence of the commands in a block, directs the command that follows, to the correct address or "register" of the system. The individual commands are thus separated by the Tab code, which precedes the digital information of each command.

The commands must be punched into the tape in a predetermined sequence throughout, and the X coordinate must always precede the Y coordinate. The End of Block code is used as before.

Interchangeable, Variable Block Format—A variation of the word address format, the interchangeable variable block format is actually a combination of the word address and tab sequential formats. The design of some systems may permit the use of either the tab or word addresses, and in some other cases, both.

This format also permits use of the Tab code for the purpose of separating (spacing) commands on the program printout, thus improving legibility; the Tab code, as punched into the tape, is then ignored by the system.

The delete code, used in making corrections and deletions when operating a tape-punching typewriter, can also be used in this format.[2]

A *fixed block* format may require commands to be entered in a fixed sequence, and with a constant number of commands (or their equivalents) in each block.

Other formats and standards have been proposed and used.

EXAMPLES OF COORDINATES AS PUNCHED IN TAPE

In using EIA standard, 1 in. wide, 8-track tape, with the BCD system and the word address format, the coordinate dimension must always be preceded by its word address, the letter X or Y, when designating the X and Y motions or axes of a machine. The same applies to the Z axis, and any additional ones.

The numerical control system may accept either a five-digit figure or a six-digit figure after the word address, depending on system design or selection. Still others are possible. Assuming that an X coordinate is 24.758 in. in its absolute dimension and the Y coordinate is 19.360 in., then the coordinates could be written as: X 24.758 and Y 19.360. It is not necessary to program or include the decimal point, and the coordinates would be programmed as: X 24758 and Y 19360.

If the system is designed to accept six digits to the right of the word address, and with the decimal point again left out, it is possible to program dimensions to the fourth decimal point (tenths of thousandths) and representative coordinates could be: X 233125 and Y 188125. The decimal point is understood, whether five- or six-digit figures follow the word address letter.

Alternatively, a large machine may require three digits to represent table or slide travel in whole inches, e.g., X 233125 (to program X 233.125 in.), its system chosen accordingly.

Also, whether five or six digits are used after the word address code, their positions must all be filled, using zeros if required (except where memory is provided, and depending on system type—see details following). For example, an X coordinate of 0.750 must be written as X00.750, if the rule for the five-digit number applies to the system.

Coding on Tape—The coordinates X 24758 and Y 19360 are shown coded and punched in tape in Figure 11–7. Note that the important parity check code is included (track No. 5).[3]

Memory Provision in NC System—When a system includes the memory feature described here, then digits that are repeated in following commands need not be programmed, provided there is no change from one figure or coordinate to the next, as applying to the particular digits that are dropped.

Examples follow, with the longer programming method in the left column and the shorter method, using memory, in the right-hand column:

X 01125	Y 01125	X 01125	Y 01125
X 03775	Y 01125	X 0377	
X 06375	Y 01125	X 063	

---

[2] For more details of specific standards and formats, see bulletins on *EIA Standards* by Electronic Industries Association, Washington, D. C.

[3] Various NC standards and tape specifications are also given in the *Numerical Index* editions, on a current basis, of the *National Aerospace Standards* of the Aerospace Industries Association of America, Washington, D.C. (Washington, D.C.: National Standards Association, Inc.).

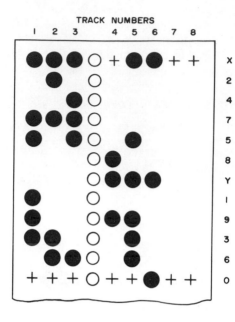

Figure 11–7. Tape codes punched for coordinate X at 24.758 in. and Y at 19.360 in.; using the word address tape format. Holes in track 5 provide parity check. Decimal point is omitted.

Program Example—The preceding coordinates are for holes Nos. 1–3 inclusive of the part in Figure 11–8. In programming such a part, all hole positions should be numbered on the drawing or print, and if possible, preferably in the sequence in which they will be drilled or machined. The coordinates for programming all eight holes, using memory as described, are then as follows:

HOLE OR POSITION NO.	X COORDINATE	Y COORDINATE	HOLE OR POSITION NO.	X COORDINATE	Y COORDINATE
1	X 01125	Y 01125	5	X 09870	Y 02750
2	X 0377		6	X 08125	Y 0250
3	X 063		7	X 05373	Y 0275
4	X 10		8	X 0212	Y 0250

It will be seen that the dimensioning, as well as the programming are on the absolute basis; the zero reference point or reference zero for the X and Y axes is at the lower left-hand corner of the workpiece in this example.

The coordinates, using word addresses, would be punched as in the example of Figure 11–7; the X coordinate precedes, followed by the Y coordinate, for each position or hole (but the Y coordinates are omitted where they remain unchanged, as explained).

This is single-quadrant programming, and in the first quadrant: all coordinates have positive values, and the plus signs are omitted. With four-quadrant programming, the reference zero would be at or near the center of the workpiece, and the X and Y coordinates would be prefaced with plus or minus signs (or the latter only, as required) to indicate the quadrant positions of the coordinates.

The preceding program example would still require the addition of further commands, such as preparatory and miscellaneous functions; these are included in the examples in Chapter 12.

Dropping repetitive digits with the memory feature can save considerable tape length, because each character, when coded, occupies one transverse row on the tape. Repetition

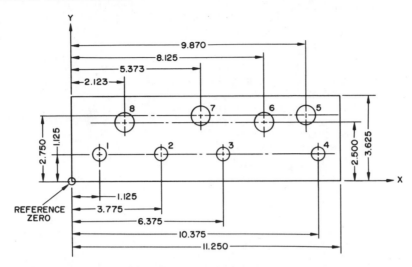

Figure 11–8. Example of part and dimensions for a two-axis, point-to-point program, using absolute dimensioning.

of the Y coordinate, as in the above example, occurs frequently where holes must be drilled or punched along a straight line. The coordinate data remain in the memory until automatically "erased" when a new coordinate or digit is programmed. The omission, if any, of digits in programming and tape punching, depends on the individual control system.

It should be noted that, for example, the digit 1 in the coordinate 19.360 is coded or represented as if it were a units digit. In other words, it is not necessary to express this digit as 10. Its value has been expressed in binary coded decimal form, and the numerical control system will recognize its actual value according to its sequence position and the coding on the tape.

STRAIGHT BINARY CODE

The straight binary (SB) system was used extensively in the early years of numerical control development, and subsequently was replaced, to a large extent, especially for positioning, by the binary coded decimal system.

Figure 11–9 shows the binary system as it has been used for the Dynapath 10 continuous-path numerical control system by The Bendix Corporation, Industrial Controls Section. (See also Figure 11–4 for the binary numbers chart, and related text.) The tape format differs from those previously described. It will be noted that certain tracks or levels are reserved for the X, Y and Z axes, for entering the applicable motion commands, and others for the feed rate, end of block, and parity codes. This example also shows two tracks reserved as spares.

Figure 11–10 gives an example of an X-motion command in the binary code, for a continuous-path program. The holes are punched in track or level No. 5, which is reserved for the X axis. The tape is read lengthwise, instead of across as in the more common and previously described formats. The five punched holes, commanding 101101001 units of X-axis motion expressed as a binary number,[4] occupy nine hole positions lengthwise of the track;

---

[4] This example, also Figure 11-10 (as well as Figure 11-6), have been the subjects of a numercial control seminar conducted jointly by The Boeing Company (Wichita, Kans.), and the American Machine Tool Distributors Association (Washington, D.C.).

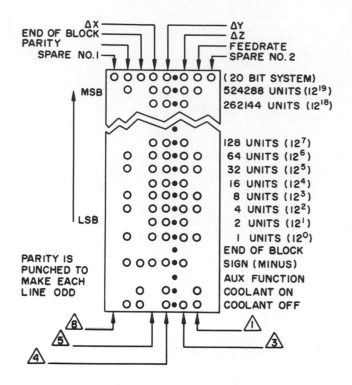

Figures 11–9 & 11–10. At top: Tape coding, using binary system, for a Bendix Dynapath 10 continuous-path control. (The Bendix Corporation Industrial Controls Section.) At bottom: Example of binary-coded tape and an X-motion command for a continuous-path program. (The Boeing Company (Wichita, Kans.), and American Machine Tool Distributors Association.)

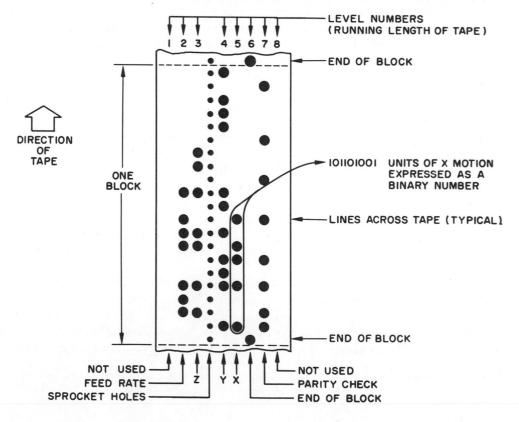

20 transverse rows are provided for the block, with an additional row for placing the end-of-block hole. It may be seen that the end-of-block code hole is in level No. 6, instead of the usual No. 8. As the track positions identify and direct the commands to their proper destinations, and all information is expressed in binary numbers, word or tab address codes are not required or employed.

TAPE LENGTHS

Punched tape is used in the form of short lengths, in loops, and in long lengths on reels. The amount or length of tape required depends of course on the length of the program, and some examples were given earlier. It also depends on the tape format employed, the type of coding used, and special features such as the use of memory. Tapes for average positioning programs can run from about 18 in. to 72 in. in length, and occasionally may reach 40 ft.–50 ft.

Tapes may run to 3,000 ft. in length for the machining of a single turbine generator frame on a $2 million numerically controlled machine tool as installed by Westinghouse Electric Corporation, Pittsburgh Works. This is an extreme case of complex work, as most tapes for general positioning do not approach such a figure.

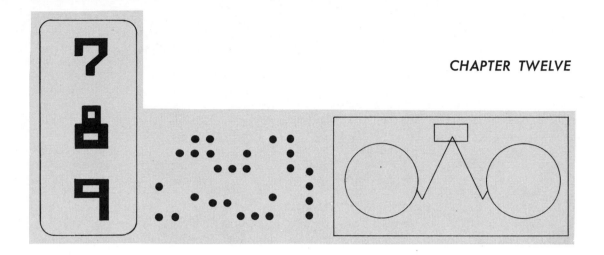

CHAPTER TWELVE

PROGRAMMING FOR POSITIONING AND CONTOURING

Programming Steps

IN ITS WIDER SENSE, PROGRAMMING INCLUDES PROCESS PLANNING—OR THE USUAL PLANNING OF THE PRODUCTION OPERATIONS—IN ADDITION TO THE STEPS FOR TAPE PREPARATION. REVIEWING THE BASIC STEPS, THEY ARE:

1. PREPARE NC COORDINATE DRAWING

FOR AN ABSOLUTE SYSTEM, USE ABSOLUTE DIMENSIONING, TAKING THE ORIGINAL DIMENSIONS FROM THE PART PRINT OR DRAWING. THIS STEP IS SOMETIMES OMITTED, AND THE DIMENSIONS FROM A CONVENTIONAL DRAWING, GENERALLY OF INCREMENTAL TYPE—UNLESS INTENDED FOR A JIG BORER, FOR EXAMPLE—ARE SIMPLY ADDED TO OBTAIN DIMENSIONS ALONG THE REQUIRED AXES.

ABSOLUTE DIMENSIONING AND PROGRAMMING ARE WIDELY USED FOR POSITIONING, AND EITHER INCREMENTAL OR ABSOLUTE FOR CONTOURING OR CONTINUOUS-PATH APPLICATIONS.

139

2. PLAN OPERATIONS OR PROCESS SEQUENCE

Determine the sequence of operations and tooling to be used, calculate cutting speeds and feeds, etc., and list all data on a process planning sheet or operations sheet, sometimes called a tooling sheet. Also list turret positions and respective tools, as may be required, also coolant details and additional relevant instructions. (The coordinate dimensions are not included at this point, but are tabulated later on the program sheets or program manuscript.)

3. PREPARE PROGRAM SHEET

Tabulate all operations on the program sheet or standard form supplied, using all cutting and tool data from the process or operations sheet, but in condensed form. Enter X, Y, and Z coordinates in their respective columns, also the miscellaneous or auxiliary functions, etc., as required. Write the positioning coordinates with their proper number of digits, using or adding zeros where required, and prefix them with X, Y, or Z letters or addresses (when using the word address tape format). Follow similar procedure for machine functions or other commands.

Coordinates and other command data for continuous-path operations are listed similarly, but they require additional consideration, as given later in this chapter.

4. PUNCH THE TAPE

When using a standard automatic tape-punching typewriter, and the BCD numbering system, the tape is automatically coded and punched by the machine as the individual characters are keyboarded. The typewriter also produces a "tape readout" (or printout) which is a duplicate of the program manuscript; it contains essentially the same data as the original program manuscript.

5. VERIFY THE TAPE

(See details in preceding chapter.) Punch a second tape for sending to the shop together with a tape readout or a duplicate of the program manuscript. File the original tape.

The setup, as planned, and the numerically controlled machining or production, can then begin.

Programming a Turret Drilling Machine

MACHINE, SYSTEM AND OPERATIONAL DATA

Machine—The machine tool of this example is an Avey Turret-Dex drilling and tapping machine. The model in Figure 12–1 has an eight-spindle turret on a vertically sliding head, a 30 in. × 40 in. bed type table, a drilling capacity in mild steel of 1½ in., 99 feed rates, and 12 standard spindle speed rates of 110 to 1,800 r.p.m., or optionally 24 speeds, with later models having 80 spindle speeds available, from 45 to 6,000 r.p.m. The machine, built by Avey Machine Tool Company, a Division of The Motch & Merryweather Machinery Co., is a relatively large drill; procedures with medium sized drilling machines are similar, however.

The NC System—The machine uses a three-axis General Electric Mark Century positioning system of absolute type (these drills may also be supplied with other systems, such as Sperry UMAC 5, Hughes, and Bendix).

Figure 12–1. An Avey Turret-Dex NC drill, used for machining the part of Fig. 12–2. (Avey Machine Tool Company.)

The Part or Workpieces—Figure 12–2 is a print of the part, of cold rolled steel, which serves to demonstrate the programming and production principles involved; the steps following are based on procedures as developed by Avey Machine Tool. The dimensions are not of the absolute type, but are given in the conventional or incremental manner, because this is a conventional shop print. The programmer adds the dimensions as given on the print to obtain absolute dimensions from the basic reference point. Operations include drilling, boring, reaming, tapping, center drilling and end milling.

Operations or Process Planning—The machining operations required, as indicated on the print, include the end-milling of a square recess, $\frac{1}{16}$ in. deep and with a radius of $\frac{3}{8}$ in. at each of its corners, this dimension being derived from the $\frac{3}{4}$ in. end mill that is specified. Hole identification Nos. 1–7 have been added to the print, but they do not necessarily indicate the machining sequences.

The next stop is to plan the sequence of operations, determine the tooling to be used, and calculate the cutting speeds and feeds, etc., listing them on a detailed process planning or operations sheet. (The coordinate data for positioning are not required at this stage.)

Machining or Production Operations—These follow, with their detailed operation numbers for use later on the program sheet. The different tools are allocated to the various

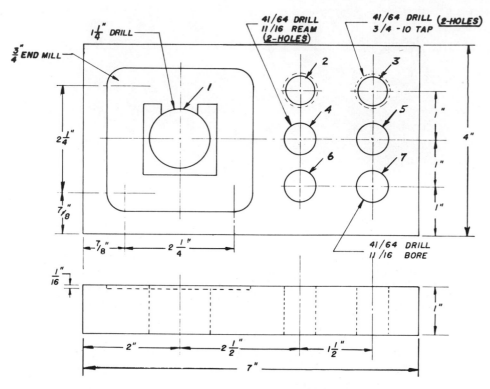

Figure 12–2. Print of part for NC programming and machining, involving typical operations. (Avey Machine Tool Company.)

turret spindles according to a setup sheet (see upper half of Table 11–1, more on which will be said later).

1. Center drill hole Nos. 1–7 inclusive, in the sequence 1, 2, 3, 5, 4, 6, and 7, with 0.187 in. or No. 5 center drill, using spindle No. 6. Operations N001 to N007. This center drilling provides starting points for the larger drills to follow, preventing their running off to one side.

2. Drill hole No. 1 with 1¼ in. drill; drill through, use spindle No. 8. Operation N008.

3. End mill recess with ¾ in. end mill, producing ⅜ in. radii at corners, with spindle No. 1. Position end mill near center of 1¼ in. hole, mill inward to "top" edge of recess, then mill all around recess or pocket in a clockwise manner, which involves four additional changes in direction (this is positioning, or rather straight-cut milling, with feed rate control). Operations N009 to N015.

4. Drill with $^{41}\!/_{64}$ in. tap drill for ¾ in.—10 tap, hole Nos. 2 and 3; spindle No. 2. Drill through, as shown on print. Operations N016 to N017.

5. Drill hole Nos. 4, 5, 6, and 7, using $^{41}\!/_{64}$ in. drill (program sequence will be hole Nos. 5, 4, 6 and 7). Use same spindle, No. 2, as for previous operation. Operations N018 to N021.

6. Bore hole Nos. 7 and 6, in this sequence, using boring tool for $^{11}\!/_{16}$ in. dia. and spindle No. 3. Operations N022 to N023.

7. Ream with $^{11}/_{16}$ in. reamer in spindle No. 4, hole Nos. 4 and 5, in this sequence. Operations N024 to N025.

8. Tap ¾ in.—10 threads per in., hole Nos. 3 and 2, using spindle No. 5. Operations N026 to N027.

PROGRAMMING AND SETUP DATA

Setup Sheet—The machining operations are planned with a setup sheet, which in this case is in four parts. The first two parts are given in Table 11, the top half giving a description of the cutting tools as used in their spindle positions, together with necessary speed and feed rates and additional data—the spindle speed and feed codes (S and F respectively), will be explained later).

The lower section of Table 11, which constitutes the second part of the four-part setup sheet, includes notes such as the X, Y, and Z offsets, and additional tool and material instructions.

The setup sheet is actually a condensed process planning or operations sheet, sometimes called a tooling sheet, which also includes drawings or sketches of the machine table dimensions, location of workpiece on table, and zero or reference positions of table, workpiece, and spindle. The positioning coordinates are tabulated later on the program sheet or manuscript.

TABLE 11

PARTIAL SETUP SHEET FOR TURRET DRILL

For the Part of Figure 12–2

SPINDLE	DESCRIPTION	DIA.	S.F.M.	CALC. R.P.M.	MACH. R.P.M.	FEED RATE	TURR. FEED	TOOL LENGTH	TOOL OFFSET	S	F
1	¾" End Mill	.750	60	306	300	.002/.008	2.4			04	05
2	41/64" Drill	.640	80	490	440	.007	3.0			05	06
3	11/16" Bore	.687	60	333	440		.5			05	01
4	11/16" Ream	.687	40	222	220	.018	4.0			03	08
5	¾"—10 Tap	.750	40	203	150	.100	15.0/14.0			02	28
6	#5 C'Drill	.187	80		1800		6.0			12	12
7											
8	1¼" Drill	1.250	80	245	1200/240	.012	2.5			10	05

1. X offset 082813—Y offset 082813.
2. Tool offset to 2" above work.
3. #8 is H.D. (5:1) spindle.
4. 110–1800 R.P.M. Range.
5. Use Tension Type Tap Holder.
6. Material—C.R.S.

Avey Machine Tool Company.

Zero Reference Point and Offset: Figure 12–3 is a sketch based on the third part of the setup sheet, a plan view of the large machine table and of the part or workpiece mounted on it. It shows the zero reference point for the coordinate dimensions, called the "table zero" in this case, as being at the front left-hand corner of the table.

The reference zero on the part itself, in relation to the table zero, has the following coordinates or offsets: 8.2813 in. on the X axis, or the longitudinal motion of the table, and 8.2813 in. likewise, on the Y axis, or transverse motion of the table. These are designated as X and Y offsets in Table 12–1, being given as: X offset, 082813; Y offset, 082813. Thus, the location of the reference zero may be chosen by the programmer as desired.

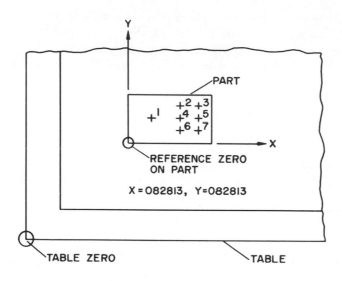

Figure 12–3. Location of part on table of turret drilling machine, and showing zero offsets.

The fourth part of the setup sheet is simply a sketch giving the side view of the machine table and column, together with the spindle, and showing the "tool offset reference" point for the Z axis, or vertical movements of the spindle; the latter is given as being 2 in. above the surface of the part.

Setup Instructions—Risers (raisings blocks) 10 in. and 5 in. high are to be placed on the table to raise the workpiece to a suitable height relative to the spindle, because it is a relatively small part for this size of machine. The part is to be clamped to the top riser on 1-in. high parallel blocks, to allow drilling or machining through the piece.

The part is to be aligned with the table zero so that its front left-hand corner is 8.2813 in. to the right of the table zero, parallel to the X axis, and inward on the table from the table zero a distance of 8.2813 in., relative to the Y axis. These dimensions are inserted into the system by manual digital input, using the X and Y zero offset switches (full-range zero shift) provided; they are ignored in the programming of the coordinates for the part itself. There are six manually set thumb switches for each of the X and Y axes, for shifting or offsetting the zero to any point on the table, as may be required.

The tools are mounted in the turret spindles usually so as to agree with the machining sequence (this order is not essential, however, as the turret spindles can be called up on tape command, in any sequence), and are set for height to the tool offset reference point, established as 2 in. above the surface of the work, from which all absolute distances for the vertical or Z axis will be taken. A separate group of five thumb switches for each spindle permits the Z reference zero to be shifted or offset downward from its normal or head-up position.

Tape Code System and Format—The EIA Standard, 1 in. wide, eight-track tape, with binary coded decimal system and word address format, is used. Tape is punched on a Friden Flexowriter. (Codes are essentially the same as those of Figure 11–6 of the previous chapter.) The control system requires that the word address code—such as X and Y—be followed by six digits, i.e., a six-digit number. Absolute coordinates are used, as the system is of absolute type. Zeros must be added or placed as required; the decimal point is omitted because it is "understood" as being located behind the second of the six digits. For example, an X coordinate of 4.5 in. is written as X045000. Similarly, a Z or vertical-axis coordinate such as 2.250 in. is written as Z022500. Programming of coordinates to within tenths of thousandths is made possible with the system.

Operation numbers, or sequence numbers, are coded by the letter N, and the number has any three digits as may be chosen to describe the block to follow. For instance, N001 for the first operation or sequence, N002 for the second, and so on.

Command Codes—The letter codes or word addresses for miscellaneous machine functions, preparatory functions, and other commands, which are in addition to the X, Y, and Z code letters, are listed with their meanings in Table 12.

TABLE 12

COMMAND CODES FOR POSITIONING, MISCELLANEOUS AND PREPARATORY FUNCTIONS *

(Footnotes given at end of Table)

COMMAND	PURPOSE AND DESCRIPTION
F Command	Spindle feed rate; F followed by two digits, e.g., F06 would specify a feed of 3 in. per min.
G80	Cancels all fixed cycles; prevents an accidental machine cycle if information is left in storage from previous operations. G80 must be programmed in the first block on all tapes, and in any block that contains a tool change (T command). The G80 command does not raise the head; should normally be used with an X, Y, and T command.
G81 and G82	Fixed cycles for normal drilling operations; head will move down at rapid traverse rate to the R dimension (see latter entry in Table). Head then feeds down to programmed Z depth at programmed feed rate. After feeding to Z depth, head retracts to R point at rapid traverse rate. G81 code provides for immediate retraction upon reaching Z depth; G82 code provides for dwell of head at the Z point until an auxiliary timer commands the up stroke.
G84	Tapping command. Head traverses down to R (the end of the rapid-traverse distance) and feeds to the Z depth. Spindle then reverses and head feeds out to R point. M06 function must be programmed in every block where a tapping cycle is desired, as a safety feature.
G85	Boring cycle. Head feeds out from Z to R dimension as under G84, but without reversing spindle. (Also used for a tapping cycle when an automatic reversing tapping head is employed.)
G86	Milling. The X and Y dimensions of the starting point must be programmed in first block. Next block should have G86 code and the necessary R and Z dimensions to place head in starting position. Each block following the Z information should include a coordinate corresponding to the end position of a straight-line milling cut. Note: Make certain that, after completion of milling, the next block for the succeeding operation contains the required codes to cancel milling cycle and raise head.
G87	"Yoke" drilling. Head traverses to R dimension, feeds through Z dimension, and remains at Z point, for new information to be read. Make certain that the final R and Z data will bring tool back out of the part.
M Functions	Miscellaneous or auxiliary functions with codes chosen to suit the individual plant's applications for up to nine auxiliaries; letter M followed by digits 01 to 09. M functions may be assigned thus:

M01–M05	Unassigned.	M08	Coolant on.
M06	Tap interlock.	M09	Air and coolant off.

Continued—Table 12

Command Codes for Positioning, Miscellaneous and Preparatory Functions

COMMAND	PURPOSE AND DESCRIPTION
M07	Air on.
	Note: M07, M08, and M09 functions remain stored in system until changed. M06 function must be programmed in every block in which tapping is required.
M00	End of cycle. Stops tape reader, "but machine motion continues until all functions read before M00 command are exhausted." This function provides for *planned stops* in the program. To resume automatic operation, push "cycle start" button. For purposes of tool change or inspection, sequence of data will normally be as follows:
	G80 X123456 Y123456 T01 M00
	This cancels the fixed cycles, then moves the workpiece to the required (unloading) position, raises head, and then stops the program.
M30	End of tape. Used at end of tape, this code is the same as M00, but in addition, will rewind tape to first stop code (usually preceding the first block). To resume automatic operation, push "cycle start" button. To bring head up at this time, use a turret command.
N	Operation sequence number. Letter N followed by any three digits as may be chosen by programmer describes block to follow; usually begins with 001, 002, etc., as N001, N002, and N025.
R	Letter R followed by four digits, e.g., R0180, describes R dimension or absolute distance (on Z axis) which the head traverses at its rapid feed rate; decimal point understood after second digit.
S	Spindle speed selection; letter S followed by two digits indicates revolutions per minute; e.g., S00, S01, and S02 may designate 187, 250, and 375 r.p.m. respectively, depending on machine model. Spindle speed ranges to be used for tapping depend on model.
T	Spindle selection, therefore, also indicates type of tool. Spindles No. 1 to 8 are programmed with a T followed by two digits; e.g., T01, T02, and T03 would select spindle Nos. 1, 2, and 3 respectively.
Z	For Z dimension on vertical or spindle axis; letter Z followed by six digits for depth of cut, including rapid traverse and feed dimensions measured from the "head up" or zero position. Decimal point understood after second digit. (For X and Y commands, see text.)

* For Avey Turret-Dex drilling machine with eight-spindle turret, and employing General Electric Mark Century positioning control. Based on Avey programming instructions. Word address system. For table positioning (X and Y) codes, and offset or zero shift provisions, see text.

Pointers on Programming—As to programming for its Turret-Dex drill equipped with this NC system, the Avey Machine Tool Company makes certain suggestions, described here as follows:

1. When programming for rapid traverse down to the R dimension, a small deceleration distance must be considered; generally, 0.2 in. is sufficient.

2. When tabulating coordinates on the program sheet (as is given here under "The Program Sheet or Manuscript," and in Table 13 following), always place the X and Y data in a block which is separate from the R and Z values. Also, place auxiliary commands with the X and Y data to decrease reading time. The G80 code (which cancels all fixed cycles) should be used wherever a G function is to be erased, and be placed with the X and Y information; the other G functions are placed in the R and Z block.

3. For safety reasons, a G80 command should always be programmed in the first block of any tape and in every block that contains a tool change, or T command.

4. If the proper G function and R and Z commands are stored, then the R and Z functions are not required for each operation.

5. The head must be indexed to effect a spindle speed change.

6. It is possible to drop trailing zeros in a program provided the preceding information and dropped digits remain unchanged.

7. Zero offset for Z axis: the thumb switches for this offset are for use only in the tape mode of operation; in the manual and setup modes they function only as positioning aids.

8. Amount of Z axis tool offset: on the Mark Century system it is 9.9999 in. maximum. A partial retraction can be carried out as a standard procedure in most cycles, but the procedure for moving around a clamp must be as in Figure 12–4. Here the programming relative to the hole positions and clamp would read this way, on the printout:

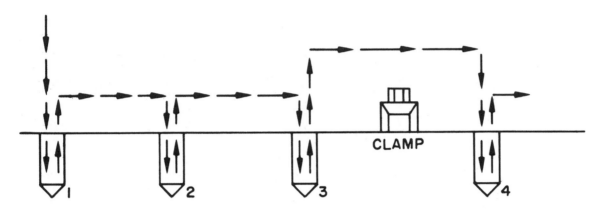

Figure 12–4. Sketch showing procedure to move around a clamp. (Avey Machine Tool Company.)

HOLE POSITION	COMMANDS				
1	g80	x100000	y100000	t01	m08
	g81	r0500	z060000		
2		x120000			
3		x150000			
4	g87	r0400	z040000		
	g80	x200000			
	g81	r0500	z060000		

Using the G87 mode of operation with the partial retraction described, is designed to result in smoother operation, with no significant time loss.

The Program Sheet or Manuscript—The information from the process planning sheet, or the equivalent set of figures, also including data as summarized in the setup sheet, are entered in their respective columns on the program sheet(s), Table 13. The operation or sequence numbers appear, in their appropriate codes, in the first or left hand column.

The absolute coordinates, together with the word addresses (letters X, Y, Z) are tabulated as shown. The absolute coordinates were obtained from the conventionally dimensioned drawing or print by addition, in the absence of an absolute type of print. A study of the part drawing, Figure 12–2, and of the preceding "Machining or Production Operations" section, will be helpful in following the entries given in the program sheet. Note the Z coordinates, for example, for center drilling, and drilling through the piece. In the second step of Operation N001, the head moves down at rapid traverse rate to a position 1.80 in., to the R point, which leaves the end of the tool at a distance of 0.20 in. from the surface of the workpiece, because the zero or reference position here is 2 in. above the workpiece surface (command R0180, then the head and tool decelerate and feed downward into the work a distance of 0.250 in. upon command Z022500, which represents the total distance from the zero or reference position to the bottom of that hole).

TABLE 13

PROGRAM SHEET

For Machining the Part of Figure 12–2

OP. NO.	"G"	"X"–"R"	"Y"–"Z"		AUXILIARIES		
N001	G80	X020000	Y020000	S12	F12	T06	M08
	G81	R0180	Z022500				
N002		X045000	Y030000				
N003		X060000					
N004			Y020000				
N005		X045000					
N006			Y010000				
N007		X060000					
N008	G80	X020000	Y020000	S10	F05	T08	
	G81	R0180	Z035000				
N009	G80	X020000	Y022000	S04	F05	T01	
	G86	R0180	Z020625				
N010			Y031250				
N011		X031250					
N012			Y008750				
N013		X008750					
N014			Y031250				
N015		X020000					
N016	G80	X045000	Y030000	S05	F06	T02	
	G81	R0180	Z032500				
N017		X060000					
N018			Y020000				
N019		X045000					
N020			Y010000				
N021		X060000					
N022	G80	X060000	Y010000	S05	F01	T03	
	G81	R0180	Z031000				
N023		X045000					
N024	G80	X045000	Y020000	S03	F08	T04	
	G81	R0180	Z032000				
N025		X060000					
N026	G80	X060000	Y030000	S02	F28	T05	
	G84	R0180	Z031000	M06			
N027		X045000		M06			
	G80	X150000	Y100000	M30	T05		

Avey Machine Tool Company.

In operation N008, as another example, the 1¼ in. diameter drill, used in spindle No. 8 (T08), at coded cutting speed and feed rate, is moved down a total distance of 3.500 in. from the spindle zero point or "tool offset reference." With 2 in. of free travel above the workpiece, and 1 in. of tool feed through the 1 in. thick piece, the programmed 3.500 in. leaves ½ in. for the drill point itself to pass or go beyond the bottom surface of the part (coordinate Z035000).

It will be noted that, where commands remain unchanged, they need not be entered in their respective columns, or programmed (this makes use of a memory feature in the system). The entire program ends with the G80 command, and the X and Y coordinates show that the part is moved clear of the spindle, to facilitate unloading.

The program sheet then goes to the automatic tape punching typewriter, which simultaneously types a copy of the manuscript—a tape "readout" or printout.

Hints on Tape Preparation—For punching the tape leader, the machine tool builder recommends the following procedure:

1. Tape feed, about 6 to 8 in. of tape length.
2. Space bars, about 6 in., to provide space for writing identification on tape.
3. Tape feed, another 6 or 8 in.
4. Stop codes, about three or four (see also M codes).
5. End of Block code for carriage return of tape punching typewriter and to indicate end of block.
6. Start first block of information or commands.

Following the last end of block code, about a foot of tape feed should be punched.

Printout or Readout—Table 14 shows part of the printout and contains the same information at the program sheet, and the two are compared, or the tape verified.

TABLE 14

PARTIAL PRINTOUT OR READOUT

n001	g80	x020000	y020000	s12	f12	t06	m08
	g81	r0180	z022500				
n002		x045000	y030000				
n003		x060000					
n004			y020000				
n005		x045000					
n006			y010000				
n007		x060000					
n008	g80	x020000	y020000	s10	f05	t08	
	g81	r0180	z035000				
n009	g80	x020000	y022000	s04	f05	t01	
	g86	r0180	z030625				
n010			y031250				
n011		x031250					
n012			y008750				
n013		x008750					
n014			y031250				
n015		x020000					
n016	g80	x045000	y030000	s05	f06	t02	
	g81	r0180	z032500				
n017		x060000					

Avey Machine Tool Company.

The Punched Tape—A section of the punched tape, involving Operations 26 and 27, is shown in Figure 12–5, together with the respective codes. Referring to the program sheet, and reading from the bottom of the tape portion in this case, the information starts with the G84 command which begins the second line under Operation N026, and proceeds to and includes M06 under Operation N027. (Note the use of the Tab code, which spaces out the commands on the printout.)

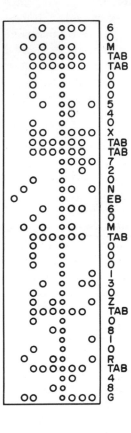

Figure 12–5. A portion of the punched tape, together with the command codes, for the part of Fig. 12–2 (read upward). (Avey Machine Tool Company.)

Machining the Part—After setting up the machine and aligning the workpiece as planned, and placing the tape in the tape reader of the system, the first part can be run off. The program sheet or the tape readout is used for following the progress of the operation and for obtaining any further information that may be required at the machine.

Programming for Continuous-Path Operations

The examples following can be applied to such operations as contour milling on a variety of milling machines and continuous-path turning on lathes.

Systems with built-in interpolation—which can be linear, circular, parabolic, or more than one of these in the same system—require only a minimum of input data. With linear interpolation, a circle arc or a curve is generated by a series of many short straight-line increments (chords, when cutting on the inside of a curve), which are automatically computed by the system.

With circular and parabolic interpolations, the increments are based on the circle arc and parabola respectively. The interpolation feature (internal interpolation) eliminates the necessity of calculating the many increments beforehand and programming them all on tape.

SPECIAL FACTORS IN CONTINUOUS-PATH PROGRAMMING

Programming for contouring or continuous-path control differs from that used for point-to-point or positioning control mainly through the introduction of these additional factors:

1. *Change Points*—A contour must be defined chiefly by the location of the change points: the positions where a curve, for example, begins and ends, or where the contour changes from a slope or taper to a circular arc, as another example. The X and Y coordinates of the change points—also the Z coordinates if the operation is three-dimensional—and additional data which describe or determine the course and shape of the contour must be given.

2. *Feed Rate Calculations*—Appropriate feed rates must be calculated for the linear, circular or other movements that comprise the cutter or tool path (or any other "path" that must be under continuous control). The calculated feed rates or feed rate codes assure that the cutter will continue to operate under proper feed rates as it encounters sharp or abrupt changes in the contour or path it is following (see also later explanations).

The calculated results may then be expressed as feed rate numbers (FRN), or as feed rate commands, prefixed by the word address letter f on the program sheet. With some systems, selected feed rates can be coded directly, using a standard EIA feed code system given in the previous chapter. With any of these methods, the feed rates then remain as programmed for each movement or span. The method of calculating or coding feed rates depends on the type of numerical control system employed.

3. *Arc Start to Arc Center Distances as X and Y Dimensions*—Continuous-path programming is frequently of incremental type, used with automatic circular interpolation. With such a control system, these dimensions, also known as the X and Y "arc offsets," must be determined and programmed in order to "position" an arc of a circle, as in Figure 12–6. These arc offsets are the distances from the start of the arc to the arc center, on the X and Y axes. For programming them with the standard word address tape format, these dimensions or offsets may be assigned the word addresses i and j.

In addition to these two dimensions for the arc, which are programmed as X and Y increments in incremental programming, the end point of the arc must also be given in X and Y increments, all of these dimensions being stated in inches.

The direction must also be specified, as clockwise or counterclockwise, common codes for these commands being g02 and g03 respectively.

Given these three specifications of an arc, programmed on tape as required, the numerical control system automatically performs the interpolation to result in the desired path.

4. *Tool or Cutter Offset*—In machining a two-dimensional contour with an end mill, for instance, it is not the centerline of the cutter or end mill which follows the contour shown and specified on the part print or drawing, but the cutter's periphery. If a "cutter offset" feature were not provided in the control system, it would be necessary to make separate calculations to allow for this factor. Provision of this feature eliminates calculating cutter offsets and simplifies manual preparation of control tape on an automatic tape punching typewriter. Computer programming may be required otherwise, and in any case, cutter offset can greatly speed up most contour programming applications.

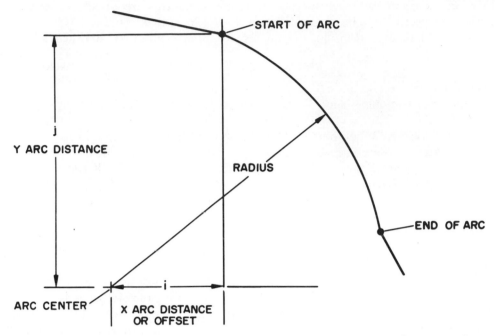

Figure 12–6. Data and nomenclature for specifying an arc for circular interpolation.

THE NUMERICAL CONTROL SYSTEM

The system of the following programming example is the TRW-3000 numerical contouring control by The Bunker-Ramo Corporation, Numerical Control Systems; the instructions and procedures are based on an example by this systems manufacturer.

The programming for this contouring operation example is incremental. The punched tape employs the EIA Standard of 1 in. width and 8 tracks, with the binary-coded decimal system and word address format. The example is for two-dimensional applications, but procedures for three-dimensional work or three-axis control would be similar, with addition of the third or Z axis.

Word Address Codes for Commands—The word address code letters for the coordinates and other main commands, the former followed by a plus *or* minus sign to indicate direction as employed in this example, are:

X-axis increment	x±	*Arc-center y distance or y offset*	*i*
Y-axis increment	y±	*Preparatory function for clockwise direc-*	
Feed rate number (FRN) or feed rate		*tion of arc or curve*	*g02*
command	*f*	*Preparatory function for counterclockwise*	
Arc-center x distance or x offset	*i*	*direction of arc*	*g03*

Additional addresses would be according to EIA standards.

Programming Steps and Rules—These are first divided according to linear or circular movement, and are as follows:

1. Linear Movement
   (a) Describe or state x and y increments in inches.
   (b) Calculate the Feed Rate Number, FRN, as $\dfrac{\text{Velocity}}{\text{Distance}}$;

   this may also be expressed as $\text{FRN} = \dfrac{\text{Feed in Inches per Min.}}{\text{Distance in Inches}}$

2. Circular Movement
    (a) Describe the end point of the arc as x and y increments in inches.
    (b) State the distances, or offsets, from the start of the arc to the arc center as i (x axis) and j (y axis) increments.
    (c) Calculate the Feed Rate Number, or FRN, as $\dfrac{\text{Velocity} \times 10}{\text{Radius}}$.
    (d) State direction of arc or curve as g02 (clockwise) or g03 (counterclockwise).

The Contouring Example—The tool center path of the example being programmed is represented in Figure 12–7. The change points, or rather the movements themselves in this example, are indicated in the drawing by the numbers 1 to 4, as they occur in their sequence. Four movements are programmed to illustrate the procedure. Cutter offset is an inherent feature of the system, and cutter or tool offset calculations need therefore not be made. The required calculations follow separately.

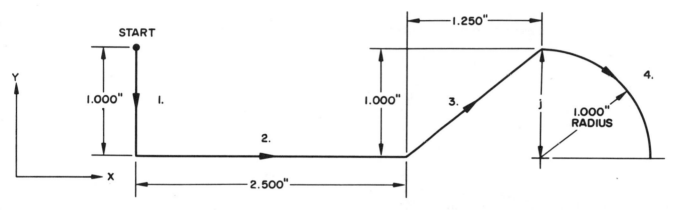

Figure 12–7. Diagram of tool center path for continuous-path programming example. (The Bunker-Ramo Corporation.)

Movements and Coordinates between Change Points—The movements required for the path or contour of Figure 12–7 (which shows the tool center path corresponding with the desired contour), with their X and Y coordinates on an incremental basis and in reference to the "start" point shown, are as follows:

MOVEMENT NUMBER	X AND Y INCREMENTS, INCHES	
1.	x = +0.000	y = −1.000
2.	x = +2.500	y = +0.000
3.	x = +1.250	y = +1.000
4.	x = +1.000	y = −1.000
	i = 0.000	j = 1.000

Calculate Feed Rate Numbers (FRN) for the Movements—The tool or movement is to proceed at 25 in. per min.; calculate the FRN data for the individual movements, using these formulas, and as explained before: for linear movement, FRN = Velocity/Distance; for circular movement, FRN = Velocity × 10/Radius.

1. FRN = $\dfrac{25}{1.000}$ = 025; this is expressed as a three-digit figure instead of 25; complete command for program sheet is f025. This three-digit figure, together with its letter prefix or word address code, in this example may be regarded simply as a code; it does not directly

represent the feed rate in i.p.m. (inches per minute), but involves a percentage type of operation in the electronic system. (See section "General Functioning of System," which follows.)

2. $\text{FRN} = \dfrac{25}{2.500} = 010$ (command, f010).

3. $\text{FRN} = \dfrac{25}{\sqrt{(1.000)^2 + (1.250)^2}} = \dfrac{25}{1.60} = 15.6 = 016$. The number is here rounded off as shown, since the feed rate does not directly affect the accuracy of the tool path; the programmed command is f016. (This calculation, as can be seen, includes a solution for the hypotenuse of the triangle formed.)

4. $\text{FRN} = \dfrac{25 \times 10}{1} = 250$, (command, f250).

Other feed rate programming methods, including EIA standard feed rate coding, may be used optionally with this system.

Complete Data for Movements—The coordinate data and feed rate information for these four movements can now be tabulated as follows:

1. y−10000   f025
2. x+25000   f010
3. x+12500   y+10000   f016
4. g02   x+10000   y−10000   j10000   f250

These data would normally be entered on a regular program sheet or manuscript for subsequent tape preparation.

Figure 12–8 shows the condensed data punched into tape, and comprising four blocks of information.

General Functioning of System—The TRW-3000 contouring control of this example is a solid-state system combining digital input—from punched tape—with analog output in the form of analog commands to the servo system. The control system functions as a pluse metering system; it selects a programmed number of pulses from a pulse train of programmed or desired frequency. The selected pulses each represent a 0.0001 in. increment of movement.

The previously calculated feed rate numbers relate to the selection of pulses to provide the desired feed rates. Axis or distance control is similarly a pulse selection or percentage operation in electronics.

The system provides an internal feed rate override, employed properly to automatically control acceleration and deceleration of machine tool slides or other controlled machine elements.

In the actual operation of the system, although the punched tape is read by the tape reader one block or one subsection at a time, machine operation is practically continuous.

This results from the following action: a block of information from the tape is first read into an intermediate storage section of the machine control unit or director, while the machine is cutting or carrying out the previous block of instructions. When the latter is completed, the system is electronically switched, so that the information from the intermediate storage circuit is transferred to final storage for use of the machine, which then starts using this new or next block of information.

After the switching has taken place, the tape reader is at work on the next block on the tape, placing it in intermediate storage, and the process continues. Because the storage circuits act as a buffer between the tape reader and the machine control unit and servos (buffer storage), their provision also makes it unnecessary to exactly synchronize tape reader and machine operation.

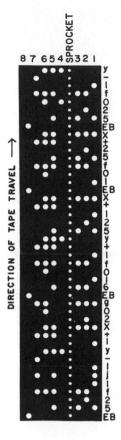

Figure 12–8. Condensed program punched into tape for four movements under contouring or continuous-path control. (The Bunker-Ramo Corporation.)

MANUAL PROGRAMMING OF CIRCLES AND ARCS

When a system does not provide interpolation, it is necessary to program a circle arc or contour in the form of a series of many short straight lines which closely approximate the desired curve and produce it within the required tolerances. When cutting on the inside of an arc, chords are involved, and on the outside, they are tangents.

For simple contour applications, and where calculations need not be extensive, the chords and any related data may be computed by means of a desk calculator. Although complex contours or paths can be dealt with in a similar way, there are cases where computer programming is the only economical or practicable solution.

Calculating Chords for Contouring Increments—When a series of short straight lines is used as chords to generate a circle arc with prescribed tolerances, the X and Y rectangular coordinates of the end point of each chord may be derived from trigonometrical calculations. (The beginning or starting point of a chord is of course the same as the end point of the previous chord.) The maximum angle subtended at the circle center, which determines the maximum length of chord that can be used, is calculated from the circle tolerance—the difference between the maximum and minimum radii.

The X and Y coordinates of chord end points are also readily derived, and they constitute the "change points" for each movement. Tables of precalculated data are of special assistance here. Chord lengths also are calculated as required.

Choices in Computer Programming Routines

Various approaches that may be required in computer programming for NC operations are exemplified in the computer routines available through the Cincinnati Numerical Automatic Program (CINAP) of The Cincinnati Milling Machine Co. Although CINTAP is a later approach by this firm, the CINAP routines serve well to illustrate principles of computer-assisted programming.

Designed for the Cincinnati Acramatic Thousand series of universal numerical control systems, the CINAP program is composed of a number of integrated computer routines for a wide range of contouring applications.

The contours or surfaces of a part to be machined are defined in terms of points, lines and circles. A "shorthand" word language of codes and numerical data is used for part definitions, machine functions, and the like. This letter code is readily learned by the programmer.

A special program sheet or form is used, on which the data relative to the computer input cards are entered. The operational data are entered on the cards and the program sheet in their CINAP codes and in the prescribed sequence.

The CINAP program is intended for numerous sizes of computers, and is written to employ multiple passes through a computer of medium size. When the program is used in its basic form, these passes constitute: (a) the data processor, for computing the path of the cutter center, and (b) the post processor, which calculates the individual chord lengths or spans to make up the cutter path, according to the maximum lengths as determined by the specified tolerance. There are some variations of this approach, for example, with a large computer, it is possible to make one operation out of the data processing and the post processing.

DATA INPUT FOR ROUTINE

The CINAP routine input to the computer consists basically of, or must take into consideration: (1) definitions of the part or contour by means of points, lines and circles, and their various combinations, identified according to CINAP conventions; (2) "special functions" such as data for feed rates, Z axis, cutter compensation, spindle and coolant, cutter offset, axis exchange (for programming the part in a plane other than the X-Y plane), etc.; and (3) the order and size of the input.

COMPUTER OUTPUT

The CINAP output data as received from the computer, and which provide all the commands necessary for operation of the control system, are punched and printed in their predetermined sequence. The final control tape may be produced from the output cards in a card-to-tape converter.

The computer output is in a format which is a combination of the tab sequential and word address formats. A Tab code identifies each group of characters (but is not used before a sequence or operation number), to make the printout more easily read; in operation, however, the Tab code is ignored by the NC system.

Numeric codes are used for preparatory functions (e.g., for point-to-point positioning or rapid traverse, with cutter compensation off; linear and parabolic forms of interpolation, and either with cutter compensation on or off; and others), also for the miscellaneous functions (such as spindle clockwise; program stop, with spindle and coolant off, i.e., the stop takes place as programmed; optional stops—for cutter change or inspection, etc.; and others). The feed rate code is based on the EIA standard, and the spindle speed code is similar.

ROUTINE FOR SPECIAL PRODUCTION TECHNIQUES

Special techniques calling for scaling, mirror image, and rotation, (also) translation, are often necessary. These are provided by a CINAP routine designated as SMART—the acronym of the preceding words.

A part program may have to be scaled to change the size of the final part as produced. A mirror image (through a built-in feature of the system) is required for producing right- and left-hand parts.

A part may be "rotated" about a point in the X-Y plane to accommodate standard stock or material size. A "translation" provides for the production of several identical parts as placed on the machine table, and from the same program.

ROUTINE FOR CONICS

Curves of all conics—parabolas, ellipses and hyperbolas—are programmed with another, or "conic-discrete point," routine.

ROUTINE FOR POCKETING

To machine pocket (cavity) contours, the CINAP system provides a special pocketing routine. As in various preceding techniques, computer programming is especially helpful here to provide commands for the repetitive machine motions that are required.

GENERAL FUNCTIONING OF SYSTEM TYPE

The Cincinnati Acramatic Thousand Series of universal numerical control systems, which combine contouring and positioning, are of absolute type. The basic system uses command data in absolute analog ratio form instead of in incremental pulses.

The numbers input is in standard binary-coded decimal form. These digital input data are converted into voltage-ratio analog form by means of precision toroidal transformers. The latter provide a voltage which is a ratio or percentage of a reference voltage; the voltage ratio is proportional to distance. The feedback system operates on the same principles. The input and feedback ratio analog values are compared to provide the feedback error signal. The digital logic and servo system is transistorized.

Either manual or computer programming may of course be employed. Both linear and parabolic interpolation may be programmed, depending on the system model selected. Parabolic interpolation is also applied to circles and circle arcs.

Parabolic interpolation, as provided by the Acramatic Thousand Series systems, is readily programmed by first giving the preparatory function code for parabolic interpolation and then the X and Y coordinates to specify the movement or span. The required parabolic curve is then automatically generated through these points by the interpolation circuitry of the system.

Control of acceleration and deceleration is automatic, through a built-in system feature. Among other system features are: full-range zero shift, direct EIA feed rate coding, feed rate override, optional cutter diameter compensation (of ± 0.999 in.), and modular construction. The standard system provides up to five axes. (The Acramatic Hundred Series, also of solid-state design, are positioning/straight-cut NC systems having features similar to the preceding.)

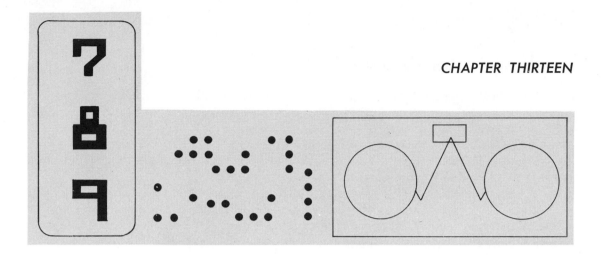

CHAPTER THIRTEEN

CHOOSING AMONG THE ALTERNATIVES TO NUMERICAL CONTROL

NUMERICAL CONTROL, ALTHOUGH IT PROVIDES A HIGHLY FLEXIBLE METHOD OF MACHINE OPERATION IN MANUFACTURING, IS NOT NECESSARILY THE ANSWER TO EVERY PRODUCTION AND COST CUTTING PROBLEM. ALTERNATIVES TO NUMERICAL CONTROL ARE AVAILABLE, AND SOME EFFECTIVE ONES WILL PROBABLY ALWAYS EXIST; OTHER "PROGRAM CONTROL" METHODS HAVE BEEN DEVELOPED AND ARE IN USE. THEY ARE ALSO COMPLEMENTARY TO NUMERICAL CONTROLS. IN CHOOSING ANY ALTERNATIVE CONTROL OR MANUFACTURING METHOD, IT SHOULD BE KEPT IN MIND THAT THE CHARACTERISTICS OF NUMERICAL CONTROL BY TAPE AND ITS INHERENT ADVANTAGES MAY NOT BE PROVIDED BY OTHER METHODS EXCEPT TO A CERTAIN DEGREE. THE ALTERNATIVE CHOSEN HOWEVER, SHOULD ADEQUATELY MEET THE INDIVIDUAL REQUIREMENTS.

159

Conventional Automatic Controls

For general comparisons between numerical control and alternative controls and methods, the three types of NC systems—as to purpose or function—can be restated: positioning, contouring, and sequence (function, or cycle) controls. The latter type is usually combined with either of the former, at least to a degree.

Controls and methods for conventional automatic operation and other high production machines may be divided into these general, main groups:

1. Cam-type controls (mechanical or electrical), employ adjustable cams or drums or other carriers, or solid cams. A modern version is the electrical function drum, making electrical contacts instead of effecting direct mechanical movements. These are chiefly sequence controls. Hydraulics and pneumatics may also be employed.

2. Automatic cycle controls for machine tables, spindles, or other moving members. These operate through adjustable trip dogs on the table or machine slide, or employ limit switches.

3. Tracer control, as applied to general purpose or fast-cycle production machines (may be used in connection with other controls). It is comparable to a contouring control.

4. Electric or/and electronic control systems using relays, static or solid-state elements with limit switches, etc., for complex operation and sequence control of transfer machines, special purpose machines, and other machine tools or equipment.

5. Precision positioning based on the use of end-measures, gages or equivalent means, together with devices to provide automatic or semiautomatic positioning movements.

Alternatives to Positioning Control

In choosing alternatives to positioning or point-to-point numerical control, it may also be necessary to provide the equivalent of feed rate or straight-cut control.

DRILLING JIGS AND RELATED TOOLING

In most cases, drilling jigs are special-purpose tooling, good for only one type of part.

The cost of drilling jigs depends on the complexity of the part to be drilled and the quantity required. The greater the quantity, the more elaborate the jig can be. Unlike the ability of numerical control, jigs and the conventional machine tools on which they are used cannot assume additional, automatic machine control over machine functions. Jigs generally demand only limited accuracy of a machine tool, as the jig holds and locates the work correctly, and guides the drills or other tools to their respective positions.

POSITION MEASURING AND READOUT SYSTEMS

Based on the equivalent of a numerical control feedback system, using transducers, "position readouts" accurately measure slide or machine element positions. The positions reached are indicated as coordinates in a relatively large, digital display or readout for each axis.

These systems provide the means for precise positioning under operator control, and without reliance on the usual setting and measuring devices—such as micrometer dials, Vernier scales, etc.—found on machine tools. They measure and indicate the exact positions that are reached, regardless of backlash in the slide whose position is being measured. Resolution can be as fine as 0.0001 in., or even finer, depending on accuracy required.

Such systems can serve as a step to full numerical control by tape. They are economical in many cases on the larger milling machines, horizontal boring mills, jig borers, and other machine tools. They provide faster, more accurate positioning than the conventional methods they replace, and are easier to use. Coordinate measuring or inspection machines make use of the same principle, and there are numerous additional applications.

CONVENTIONAL POSITIONING SYSTEMS ON MACHINE TOOLS

Jig Boring Positioning Systems—Precision work positioning or locating systems as incorporated in conventional jig borers and combined precision boring and milling machines are used for tool work and small and medium production lots where considerable precision is required. The positioning or locating systems may be based on precision coordinate lead screws, precision scales with optical devices, precision end measures with dial indicators, or electric and electronic positioning measuring devices. Operation is usually under manual control. Jig-borer time is usually too expensive for ordinary and medium-tolerance work.

TEMPLATE POSITIONING CONTROL

To position work with the use of a template as in piercing and drilling, a stylus or plunger is inserted in the holes of a template, one after another; this causes the workpiece or table to be moved and positioned in accordance with the hole locations in the template. This procedure is distinct from drilling through a template, placed over the work, to act as a drill jig.

Some auxiliary positioning tables for drilling use the template-control method, with the template and plunger or shot pin located out of sight or underneath the table.

Positioning Provisions on Other, Standard Machines—Positioning aids or devices on conventional layout drills (which may be of leadscrew type), and as provided on standard horizontal boring, milling and drilling machines, and on various milling machines, form alternative choices to jig borer positioning, and usually for larger components and work which does not require jig borer accuracy (the latter may start at plus or minus 0.0001 in.).

DEVICES FOR POSITIONING TABLES

Auxiliary positioning tables of non-numerical control type may be installed on drilling or other machines. They may employ template positioning, or devices using adjustable, indexable length stops or rods, mounted in or actuated by an indexing roll; the latter operate similarly to the indexing stop roll for controlling length positions on a turret lathe, for example.

Alternatives to Contouring Control

TRACING OR COPYING

Tracer control is used for a variety of contour machining operations; a stylus, following or tracing the contour of a cylindrical master or a flat template of the correct shape, causes the tool to reproduce the shape on the workpiece. The subject is dealt with separately in later selections of this chapter.

NUMERICAL CONTROL WITH COMBINED TRACER CONTROL

With this system, a variation of numerical positioning control is combined with tracer control, using the latter for taking contouring cuts, as described later in the chapter.

PHOTO-ELECTRIC CONTROL OR SCANNING

Contouring control by photo-electric tracing (photo-cell method—with phototube, or phototransistor devices) has been applied extensively to contour flame cutting machines. These systems trace directly from the lines of a drawing, or may employ a template, to control the path of one or more cutting torches. In the latter application, accuracies comparable to those of machining are not required.

The principle has also been applied to contour sawing; efforts are also made to adapt photo-cell tracing or optical scanning to additional operations. The general principle can be regarded as a variation and extension of tracer or copying control.

PEGBOARD OR PLUGBOARD CONTROL WITH ADDED TRACER

This machine "programming" method, a switching system, is combined with tracer control in order to produce contours, as explained in a following section of this chapter.

ADVANCED TEMPLATE CONTROL

A development in the special use of templates to provide the heart of a machine control is the Bullard "Templa-Turn" system by The Bullard Company. The control is a closed-loop (feedback-type) hydromechanical servo system; its precision feedback operates in conjunction with a precise, rotary template unit.

Used on Bullard "Templa-Turn" twin-spindle chucking machines to produce contoured and other work, with simplified, adjustable tooling developed for these machines, the arrangement is more than a control, and can be regarded as a manufacturing system in itself. Designed for rapid, automatic production, the system controls the operations cycle as well as the contours of the parts machined. Short changeover and setup times, together with improved dimensional accuracy, are featured in the concept.

The templates are made by the use of punched tape on this machine tool builder's NC template milling machines.

Alternatives to Sequence (Function) Control

Most of the preceding alternatives have dealt with positioning and contouring, instead of the control or sequencing of machine functions as such. Numerical control can also take over the control of additional machine functions such as cutting speed and feed changes, automatic tool-changer operation, turning the coolant on and off, and generally controlling all the events in a machining cycle.

With the exception of switching systems such as pegboard control, and cam-operated automatics, or systems using similar principles, the control of such machine functions is not carried out by the alternative methods *per se*. Numerical control can combine all of these functions, with the degree of automation as desired.

The more recently developed systems for controlling the sequences of machine operations or machine functions include plugboard or pegboard control, electrical switching systems such as "staging panel" controls, newer and improved versions of the electrical function drum (electrical equivalent of mechanical cams), and "fluidic" controls. They are discussed separately in following selections.

FUNCTION DRUM SYSTEM AND ITS APPLICATION

The Gisholt Masterline ABC (Automatic Bar-Chucking) lathe serves as a good example of using a control and "programming" system which is an alternative to NC operation. The ABC turret lathes, built by Gisholt Corp. (Gisholt Machine Company, Division of Giddings & Lewis Machine Tool Company), accommodate both bar and chucking work. They illustrate the important electric function drum principle as applied to modern machine tool operation and control.

Principles of Operation—The details of the electric function drum and other provisions for setting up the machine cycles and for controlling machine functions such as spindle speeds and feeds, are arranged in a manner to simplify both setup and operation.

There are three main control areas: the controls and adjustment for the hexagon turret, which carries the main complement of tools (six tools); the controls and settings for the cross slide (which has two tool positions, front and rear); and the cycle selector switches on the control panel at the headstock. The switches on this panel are not programming switches, in the sense of programming a pegboard system, for example, but incorporate the necessary control switches and permit various cycles of operation; they include such controls as dials for setting independent dwell timers (for allowing a tool to dwell or clear itself at the end of a cut) for each turret station, also for the front and rear cross slide positions, a deep-hole drilling control, and collet chuck operation control, among others.

Control of Hexagon Turret; Function Control Drum—The function control drum and its adjustments, also the adjustments for the feed trips for setting the length of stroke or strokes (length of travel) of the turret slide, are located directly at the turret end of the machine, Figure 13–1. The function drum is connected to the hexagon turret mechanism by a chain, and revolves as the turret is indexed or rotated to its respective cutting positions.

The function drum has cam buttons which are easily adjusted to control the various functions. These cam buttons operate the limit switches.

The function controls, at the turret end, control such elements and functions as traverse and feed trips of the turret, independent feed rates for each turret station, selection of 16 available spindle speeds, selection of cycle start and stop, or continuous cycle bar feed, opening and closing of collet chuck, front and/or rear tool operation, and others.

Setup Similarity; Standard Tooling—Setting up is basically similar to that of a standard or manually controlled turret lathe, except for the function drum, and since the tooling is also similar or the same, operator training for these lathes is simplified and fairly rapid.

Lot Sizes—As the setting of all the machine functions and preselection of cycles is relatively fast, and the turret tooling itself is of standard type, setups are quite rapid, making the entire control system and machine suitable for single parts, short and medium runs, as with manually operated turret lathes, as well as for high production runs.

Built-In Alternative Controls

Machine tool builders often provide alternative choices in the method of control and the degree of automation desired, in machines of the same basic type. In some cases, the alternative methods of control are present in one and the same machine or model; in other cases, the choices are made by selecting from several basic models, each with a different type of control or operation method. With either of these approaches, it is frequently possible to progress by stages, from conventional control to full tape control. It is well to consult

Figure 13–1. Control system details at turret end of Gisholt ABC lathe. Cover has been removed above function control drum (top). (Gisholt Corp.)

with the individual machine tool builder in making such choices, stating the nature of the work, the tolerances, the quantities of parts required, and how often they will be required, and related production and economic factors. Examples of such choices follow.

THREE CONTROL CHOICES IN SINGLE-SPINDLE AUTOMATICS

A choice of three control methods can be provided on various models of single-spindle automatic chucking machines and automatic bar machines (automatic turret lathes for chucking and bar work) built by The Warner & Swasey Company. Changes from one control system to another can be made in a matter of minutes, once the type of control or mode of operation has been selected to suit the type of work and quantity required.

Tape Operation—Numerical tape control is one of three types of operation available on these machines. The other two methods are regular automatic operation and manual operation, as will be described. Tape operation is employed for jobs which can be planned in advance and may be repeated from time to time.

Regular Automatic Operation—The machine is used under its regular automatic control system, basically of electric function-drum type, for work which may come to the shop at short notice and for single parts or small lots which may have to be started on immediately, without tape programming. This method also makes shop scheduling more flexible, because parts can be run off when no tape-programmed jobs are available to finish a shift, for example.

Figure 13–2 shows an operator adjusting mechanical trip blocks on the function or cycle control drum; these, together with pins installed as required, enable the drum to complete the necessary electrical circuits at the proper points to provide a desired sequence of speeds and feeds, turret station selection, stroke length, and other machine functions, in the operational cycles.

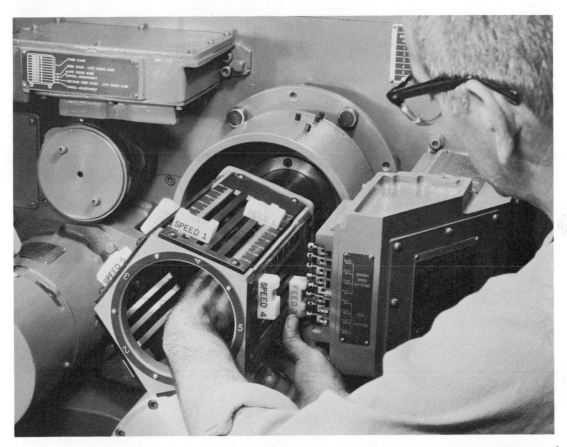

Figure 13–2. Setting mechanical trip blocks of the electrical cycle control drum on a W & S single spindle automatic lathe. (The Warner & Swasey Co.)

Manual Operation—This mode is chiefly for setups, and for checking during a production run.

Lot Sizes and Planning—Determination of economic lot sizes for production is of lesser importance with this type of machine, for the operating method is readily chosen to suit the job and circumstances.

Single parts or small batches are produced under regular automatic operation, and when no time is available for tape programming. Operation by tape may be used for runs where the planning and control over speeds, feeds, and other operating conditions, characteristic of numerical control, are to remain the functions of management through the production engineering or equivalent department.

The three-way control also makes possible the more gradual introduction of numerical control as may be desired.

MACHINE SERIES WITH PROGRESSIVELY ADVANCING CONTROLS

As an example of choices in machines leading to progressively higher degrees of automation, and ending in numerical tape control, a series of six models of drilling machines built by the Brown & Sharpe Manufacturing Company may be taken. The concept is designed to satisfy a wide range of drilling requirements and capital equipment outlays.

The series consists of turret drilling machines for drilling, tapping, reaming, counterboring and similar operations. The drills and their controls progress from manual operation to fully automatic operation with tape control for positioning, and automatic spindle cycle, as follows:

1. Manual operation—involving hand operations for work positioning, turret indexing, and tool feeds. (Drill jigs would be used for "positioning" in production work; alternatively, auxiliary non-NC work positioning tables are available, employing the template positioning method.)

2. The same machine as in (1) above, but equipped with power indexing of the six-spindle turret.

3. Automatic operation (of the basic machine, or No. 1 preceding), together with power indexing of the turret, and automatic cycle of turret spindles (cycle and depth control, by means of adjustable, circular cams and limit switches). Automatic operation includes rapid traverse of spindle to the work, power feed control, rapid spindle retraction, automatic index, adjustable feed rate for tapping, and automatic reversal of the tap at predetermined depth. This machine may also be operated manually.

4. Tape operation for positioning of table, but with manual operation for turret indexing and tool feed. (Visible and audible signals are provided for the latter.)

5. Tape control plus automatic cycle of spindle head, but with manual indexing (machine otherwise the same as in No. 4).

6. Fully automatic operation—tape control for positioning of table as before (two axes control), with automatic cycles for spindle head and automatic indexing. (Nos. 4, 5, and 6 are B & S Turr-E-Tape drill models.)

When processing very small lots, of from 5 to 10 pieces, the fully automatic model (choice No. 6 above) is generally operated manually as far as indexing of the turret and handling of the spindle are concerned. Positioning of the table however, is still controlled by tape. (Tape programming can be manual, or computer-assisted, using the company's SNAP program—Simplified Numerical Automatic Programmer.)

Pegboard or Plugboard Control

Pegboard control or pegboard programming, also known as the plugboard system, is a switching system for programming or determining all the events of a machining cycle, by presetting them on a control panel. Pins or "pegs" are inserted in the panel in the advance programming or setting up to control or complete the various circuits as they come into operation one after another. A perforated template or card can be used through which the pegs are inserted to repeat the setup at a later date, or to speed it up.

When applied to a milling machine, such as a bed-type production milling machine, pegboard control competes with point-to-point or positioning control of the type which also has rate control included. When a tracing system is used in connection with pegboard control, then the entire system also competes with continuous-path numerical control, although not necessarily in every case.

Pegboard controls as currently used do not compete with positioning systems used in such operations as drilling, tapping, and counterboring, or boring with rotating tools, on numerically controlled drilling machines, for the operating factors there are different.

An advantage of pegboard control is that the program can be "stored"—a punched template or card can be used to reset the pegs for a repeat run, without additional programming. However, table dogs that trip limit switches to control the length of slide or table travel, must still be adjusted in such cases; an alternative is to preset the dogs on removable rails, and store these assemblies for repeat production runs.

A good example of pegboard control is the Telematic system, introduced as a new automatic milling machine cycle control by The Cincinnati Milling Machine Company.

General Principle of Telematic Control—The control panel resembles a pegboard in appearance. With the use of pegs inserted in their appropriate positions, the system controls all functions or movements of the machine and also auxiliary operations, such as work clamping or indexing.

For each of 14 separate functions that can be controlled, there is a horizontal row of 24 holes, which allows the operator to peg in or program complex automatic milling cycles involving up to 24 steps or "events." Pegboard panels having more than 24 positions are also available. (These data refer to the Cincinnati Telematic control as originally introduced.)

Setting up involves placing pegs in the appropriate holes; in addition, trip dogs must be positioned to limit machine table travel and the spindle carrier travel (the machine type involved has a rise-and-fall spindle carrier). The trip dogs, which are positioned on the machine table and spindle carrier as noted, initiate each new action, and the Telematic control directs the action.

A stepping switch scans the control board one step at a time, and it initiates all functions as indicated by the placement of the pegs. When the relay scans the "reset" position, it automatically returns to its starting point, ready to begin a new cycle.

Functions Programmed—The machine functions which can be programmed with the Telematic pegboard control include:

Table feed to right or left	Quill advance
Table or carrier rapid advance	Tracer control
Spindle carrier up or down	Spindle rotation
Constant or slow feed for precision positioning	Fixture control (clamp or index)
Dwell	Reset

Setup Features—An events selector switch is provided to simplify setup; it positions the machine elements to any selected point in the cycle when a push button is depressed—the next action is then initiated without waiting for the trip dog to function.

During setup, if the operator wishes to determine where the machine is in its cycle, he turns the selector switch, and when he has reached the active event in the cycle, a panel light comes on. In addition, the operator can stop the machine at any part of the cycle, and resume the cycle without returning to the original starting point.

Tracer Control—For contouring operations, tracer control is readily programmed into the cycle, as with any other machine function.

Additional Operational Features—Accurate stops within 0.001 in. can be programmed. In addition, a single cycle can accommodate several depths of cut; it may be necessary to bypass trip dogs in order to reach the final depth.

A trip dog is not activated unless its function is pegged into the control board required for a particular event in the cycle. Sometimes it may be necessary for one event to follow another very closely. In such cases, the trip dog for the second event is simply set in a different T-slot in the table. It will then actuate its own event, even though the first-event trip dog has not fully released its plunger.

For really complex cycles, special attention should be paid to any closely set dogs. When thus set, the latter are normally used at slow traverse rates; therefore it is important to be sure that these dogs are not overriden at rapid traverse rate at some later portion of the automatic cycle.

Templates for Repeat Jobs—Plastic templates can be superimposed over the Telematic pegboard control panel when they have holes punched for a certain program or job, to speed up the insertion of the pegs on future or repeat jobs.

Cost and System Comparisons—Pegboard control involves a lower initial capital investment than numerical control. The price of a pegboard control system may be approximately one-third that of a numerical rate controlled positioning system. No special tools and no cams are required or need be stored for producing specific cycles. However, trip dogs must be set and adjusted for each new type of part that is to be machined, an operation which is not necessary with numerical control. To preserve trip dog settings for future use, it is possible to mount the dogs on replaceable rails, which are then stored for repeat runs.

SOLID-STATE PLUGBOARD CONTROL

The Telematic plugboard control was succeeded by the Telematic II plugboard cycle control system. In the design of this control, which is of modular type, The Cincinnati Milling Machine Company employs solid-state devices; stepping switches, servos, and feedback devices are not used. The system provides for manual override, and a tracer can be included in a machine program.

Figure 13–3, an overall view, shows plugs being inserted to program a milling operation under Telematic II plugboard cycle control. The system normally provides for 15 machine functions and 60 events or steps. Trip dogs and limit switches are used on the same principle as before. Signal lights on the control panel show which event is in operation. The system may be employed as a sequence or cycle control for a variety of manufacturing operations.

PLUGBOARD WITH DIAL INPUT

The addition of digital dial input provisions for positioning to a plugboard system, results in a form of numerical control. An example is the Opro-Turn system on an engine lathe built by The Springfield Machine Tool Company; it employs Cincinnati Telematic III plugboard control incorporating dial input circuitry.

Tracer Control

Tracing is the main alternative to numerically controlled contouring, and is a well proved control technique for contour work. It will most likely be used, in its own area of application, for some time to come. Before the advent of numerical control, tracer control had become indispensable for many contour machining operations.

Tracer control, or tracing, also known as copying and duplicating, and as profiling

Figure 13–3. Operator inserts plugs in a Telematic II plugboard control panel to program a milling machine. (The Cincinnati Milling Machine Company.)

(generally if of two-dimensional types), when compared with numerical contouring or continuous-path control, is probably best applied by following these three general rules:

1. *Use tracer control when uncomplicated templates are required, and numerical control for work requiring complex templates or masters.*
2. *Favor tracer control over numerical control when relatively large quantities are required, and production-type tracer machines are available.*
3. *Use TC (tracer control) for two-dimensional work, and numerical control for three-dimensional applications, generally speaking.*

If a new installation is being planned, and the choice is to be made between tracing and numerical control, it is advisable to include cost and application engineering presentations from manufacturers who produce both types of machines, when planning and considering recommendations.

Ordinarily, tracer control cannot provide a complete machine tool operation program in the manner of tape control, which can control operation sequences and machine functions as well. Tracer control is usually directed to the machining of contours, also tapers or slopes. In turning operations—tracer control is used for shouldered work—step shafts, and the like; here it competes, within its scope, with numerical positioning control incorporating feed-rate or straight-cut control.

169

WHERE TRACING OR COPYING IS USED

Tracing is now applied to most of the basic machining operations, such as turning, boring, facing, milling, shaping, planing and grinding, and to their many variations. Tracing systems are used on practically all standard machine tools, also on production machines of somewhat special nature, designed for using the tracer principle for operations such as turning shafts requiring various profiles, diameters or tapers, in quantity. In addition, some standard turret lathes have optional tracing equipment for contour work and for turning the longer tapers. A tracer system may be a portable unit which can be moved from one general-purpose machine tool to another type (with some modification), or it may be incorporated in a machine tool which is specially designed for tracer machining.

Although the type of work performed is similar to that for numerical contour control, selection of either method should be subject to the inherent capabilities of the two types of control. Complexity of a workpiece required in small or medium lots may dictate the use of numerical control, whereas parts of lesser complexity, and if required in large quantities, can employ tracer-controlled machines designed for faster machining cycles, to better advantage. The cost of making the template can often be the deciding factor in making a choice between the two systems. Work includes both the production of parts and the machining of tools—such as dies and molds on die sinking milling machines.

Tracer control applies chiefly to metal cutting (machining) operations (and in a similar principle, to flame cutting); it is normally not applied to metal forming, punching, or piercing, and similar operations; piercing usually involves positioning control or positioning functions, for the spacing and location of holes. Metal spinning, however, can be under tracer control.

COMPARING TRACER AND NUMERICAL CONTROLS

The characteristics of tracer control or copying, when applied to machining, and as reflected by its advantages and disadvantages, are listed in Table 15.

TABLE 15

COMPARISONS OF TRACER CONTROL AND NUMERICAL CONTROL

ADVANTAGES OF TRACER CONTROL

TRACER CONTROL	NUMERICAL CONTROL—REMARKS
No tape programming required, but template design and template making times must be considered	Programming for numerical control may not be justified
Templates or masters are inexpensive when profiles or contours are simple	(Templates are replaced by programming)
Equipment for the simpler application is relatively low in cost (but costs are higher for production-type machines, although usually still below NC types)	Cost depends on complexity, such as number of axes in system
Tracing or copying attachments (where such control is not built in) are portable—may be moved from one machine to another, with modification, in various cases	NC system usually remains with same machine although controls can be modified or arranged to operate several types of machines
Fast machine cycles on production type tracer lathes and similar machines	Slower cycles when compared with high production tracer equipment

Continued—Table 15

Comparisons of Tracer Control and Numerical Control

TRACER CONTROL

Tracer control can be combined with a numerical control positioning system of proper type to provide contour control.

Particularly economical for special, small tool work, and small quantities of special small parts, if contours not too complex

NUMERICAL CONTROL—REMARKS

Numerical contour control self-sufficient in this regard

Programming may cost more than the equivalent templates or models for tracing or copying

DISADVANTAGES OF TRACER CONTROL

TRACER CONTROL

Templates expensive if contours complex, and may have to be made on numerically controlled machines

Scope of control: one main function only—continuous-path control over the tool; no control over general machine functions and operation sequence

Tracer control not intended or designed for point-to-point positioning for hole location, as in drilling, boring, piercing, etc.

Templates must be accurate, as inaccuracies are reproduced in workpiece

Templates or masters depend on operator skill for accurate setting up

Setup time may be greater than with numerical control

Less flexibility may be present as to fixture or work holding requirements; fixture costs may be higher

NUMERICAL CONTROL—REMARKS

Tape programming takes place of templates

NC system can take over additional functions besides positioning, contouring, and positioning with rate control

NC systems may be chosen according to type of control required

Numerical control accuracy is determined by the system; program accuracy is subject to tape verification and proving. No templates are involved

Initial alignment of the workpiece may not be so critical

Tape programming takes the place of many setup functions

Fixtures or workholding methods generally relatively simple

TYPES OF TRACING OR COPYING SYSTEMS

Tracer control systems may be hydraulic, electromechanical, pneumatic, electrohydraulic, air-hydraulic, or electronic. Still other methods have been devised. Various improvements have been made and the scope of applications extended over a period of time. (Details of a tracer control system follow in the section dealing with an example of a combined numerical control and tracer system, as employed on the Seneca Model 400 automatic tracer lathe, built by the Seneca Falls Machine Co.)

TEMPLATES OR MASTERS

There are three general types of templates and masters or models used in tracer machining or copying to reproduce the workpiece—flat templates; cylindrical models or masters for shaft turning and similar work; and multi-dimensional, or three-dimensional masters.

Flat templates may be used with practically any type of system or machining operation, if the copying system is designed to accommodate them, while cylindrical models are generally confined to lathe work, especially shaft turning in quantity. The first part off the machine, made under conventional operation, can serve as the master for producing the rest of the lot by copying.

Template making usually involves considerable manual or toolroom work. The same holds true for three-dimensional masters.

Preliminary layout, trial cuts and measurements, together with numerous corrections and hand work, can raise the price of a template or master considerably, therefore, extremely complex masters may be produced more economically by programming them on tape and producing them on an NC machine. If, however, the quantity of parts required is not large, the entire work may be completed under numerical control, obviating the necessity of a template.

In one simplified method for making templates, except the more complicated types, without preliminary layout or cut and try machining, the work is carried out with an attachment which may be mounted on practically any vertical spindle milling machine or other machine with reasonably accurate table positioning leadscrews or aids. The method employs a device known as the Mimik Templator (by Mimik Tracers Inc.). The adjustments and motions of the device and the machine tool are manipulated to cut out a thin template of the desired shape, according to the dimensions and other data given on the print of the part to be made. The thin template is reinforced by sheet plastic, on both sides. As pressure of the stylus, which follows the contour of the template to reproduce the same contour in the workpiece, is relatively light, wear on the template is negligible.

Template design should not be left to the machine operator or shop, but treated as a production engineering function in order to assure best results with tracer machining.

COMPARISON OF PRODUCTION COSTS

For a comparison of production costs using tracer and numerically controlled machining, see the comparisons for turning a shaft by three different methods (the third being conventional operation) in Chapter 7.

Combined Numerical and Tracer Controls

An example in which numerical control is combined successfully with tracer control is the Seneca Falls 400 automatic tracer lathe. This production lathe, by Seneca Falls Machine Co., is normally furnished with a point-to-point NC system having a direct reading decimal dial input. Punched tape input may be substituted, to replace the dial input if desired.

Multiple passes may be taken with numerical positioning control over diameters and lengths. The final pass or finishing cut is always under tracer control, however; only one master template is required, and it is made to the finished dimensions of the part. Facilities for as many as 10 passes can be provided.

Figure 13–4 shows the electromechanical tracer controlled carriage arrangement, mounted on the upper bed of the machine, and which is driven by an enclosed feedscrew, in this case also referred to as leadscrew. The template is shown at the front of the carriage, on the template rail. The machine control station, with numerical dial input and other operator controls, is at the top left.

An automatically indexed, two-position tool block may be seen on the overhead carriage slide. In its use, roughing passes can be made with a carbide tool, and a finishing pass with either a carbide or oxide (ceramic) cutting tool. For long production runs, rough turning may be performed with multiple tools on the lower carriage, and finish turning with a tracer tool on one or more overhead carriages.

Figure 13–4. Tracer carriage arrangement, shown at top right, of Seneca Falls automatic tracer lathe that combines numerical dial input with tracer control. (Seneca Falls Machine Co.)

PROGRAMMING THE MACHINE

Programming of the automatic lathe by the operator involves dialling the system for the starting and ending positions for each cut or pass; dialling in the desired diameters for each cut (except for those cuts or diameters controlled by the template); setting a selector switch for the number of passes; and selecting the sequence of slide operations. (The calibrated dials read in three decimal digits—inches, tenths and hundredths of inches; no diameter dial setting is required for the finish cut, which is determined by the tracer template.) Pressing the "cycle-start" button initiates the automatic production cycle.

The reference points or lines for dialling in the command dimensions are the face of the spindle (the flange face of the spindle nose) for lengths, and the center line of the spindle for diameters. These references establish the "coordinate frame" of the machine for this dial input.

THE CONTROL SYSTEM

The system employs two sets of potentiometers, one set or group for feedback, the other for input. Feedback potentiometers, or pots, of 25-turn type are geared to the carriage drive mechanism. When electrically excited, they produce a voltage, and additionally their ratio of gearing is such that 1 in. of carriage movement equals 1 volt (and therefore, 0.001 in.

of carriage movement equals 1 mil volt). There are two feedback pots, one for the start-cut position and the other for the end-cut position.

"Command" pots for numerical input are of 10-turn type, and are mounted in the machine control station or operator's control panel. Dials, calibrated in three decimal digits, are mechanically connected with these input or "command" potentiometers. When the latter are electrically excited, they produce a voltage which is proportional to the dial setting.

Figure 13–5 is a diagram of the carriage position control system on this automatic lathe. Standard relays form the basic machine logic. As a group, the relays permit automatic sequencing of the machine. They also provide the necessary interlocking action for both manual or automatic operation. Functioning of the entire measuring system is based on comparison of the command voltage with the feedback voltage; the system senses the magnitude and phase of the difference or "error" and causes a direct current feed motor to drive the carriage in the required direction so that the error is reduced to zero. To prevent overshooting, the feed motor is automatically slowed down by means of a separate amplifier channel as the carriage approaches the dialled position. As soon as the command and position voltages coincide, the feed motor stops and the feedscrew is automatically and magnetically braked. ("Carr." refers to carriage in Figure 13–5.)

The dial input for diameter control also operates in conjunction with a feedback potentiometer. The reference for the diameters, as noted, is the spindle centerline. The various input dials on the machine control station are arranged in vertical rows, and a stepping switch in the panel automatically selects each row or pass in the required sequence.

Tracer System—The Seneca Falls electromechanical closed-loop tracing system consists of four basic parts—a tracing head or stylus, which contacts and senses the form of the template; a mechanical power or torque amplifier which positions the cross slide of the tracer carriage, and is speed sensitive; an electronic amplifier; and master template. The tracer system is shown diagrammatically in Figure 13–6.

The tracer control determines the final size, which is not under dial control, and the contour of the workpiece. In this mode of operation, the stylus assembly senses an electrical error of specific phase and magnitude which is amplified and employed to command the mechanical power amplifier to respond at the appropriate speed and direction to reduce the error to zero. The mechanical power amplifier therefore serves essentially as a servo-mechanism.

A special feature of this tracing system, aside from other patented features of the control, is the ability to take a semi-finish cut under template control, using the same template as for the finish cut. This is accomplished through the provision of the two nulls, or a "bias," which leaves a predetermined amount of stock on the workpiece for the finishing pass.

The entire system of the Seneca Falls 400 automatic tracer lathe incorporates provisions for interlocking the electrical and mechanical functions of the lathe, to assure that correct sequencing is carried out. Fast operational cycles are obtained in the machining of shaft-type as well as other parts. The lathe uses a 40 h.p. motor for the main drive. The system is designed to execute tracing operations at carriage rates up to 60 in. per min.

Additional Controls

SWITCHING AND PRESETTING SYSTEMS

Several types of electrical switching systems have been evolved for presetting machine functions on automatic turret lathes and other machine tools. One type is the "staging

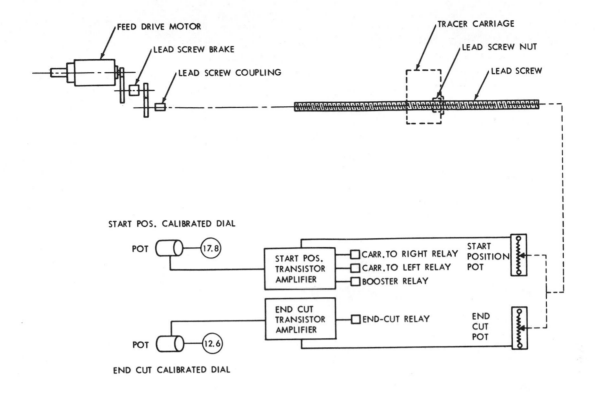

Figures 13–5 & 13–6. At top: Diagram of NC positioning system for the carriage on the combined numerical and tracer control automatic lathe. (Seneca Falls Machine Co.) At bottom: A diagram of the tracer control system on the automatic tracer lathe. (Seneca Falls Machine Co.)

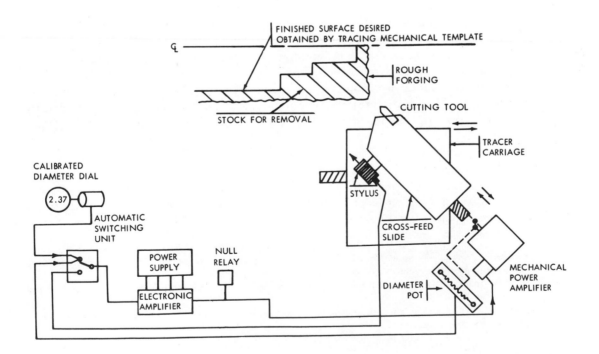

panel" control—in which switches on the programming or staging panel are preset to control machine functions and their sequence. Toggle switches, pushbuttons, or selector dials may be employed to make the settings for the controlling circuits; information may be stored in relay logic or memory circuitry; both positioning and sequence control may be provided in a system. Basically, however, such systems are usually sequence or function controls, producing results similar to those from a plugboard sequence or cycle control. (If digital dial input and feedback are provided, it moves the system into the numerical control class, even if tape is not used.)

These systems feature shorter setup times than are usually possible with conventional automatic machines. Also, to some degree, advance "programming" may be possible by indicating the control settings on setup sheets that simulate the staging or programming panel (a method similar to the principle of using a template to set a plugboard control panel).

"FLUIDIC" CONTROLS

Pneumatic and hydraulic control elements may be adapted to form complete NC systems, making use of developments in "fluidics." Air operated fluidic devices, designed to perform the functions of such control elements as relays, limit switches, and solid-state logic elements, have been used to provide machine tool sequence controls and controls for other industrial applications.

Simplicity, greater reliability, and lower maintenance and initial costs, are advanced as features of fluidic circuitry, the latter going beyond conventional air and hydraulic systems. To be determined with a period of extended use and further development are such criteria as speed of response, operational factors, and testing techniques in maintenance.

Alternative Choices Within Numerical Control

Manual digital (dial) input in a system, stopping short of "full" numerical tape control, is an alternative within the numerical control concept itself. It provides automatic positioning and feedback, as with most NC systems, but tape preparation is not required.

The commands are entered manually into the stores or memory of the control system, as by means of decade switches—with different sets of dials, thumb wheels, or pushbuttons—for making settings on a decade basis, in inches, tenths of an inch, hundredths, thousandths, and possibly ten-thousandths of an inch, to insert the coordinate or positioning information. Further, a complete block of information may be dialled in or inserted manually, including preparatory and miscellaneous function codes. (See also preceding description of dial input circuit elements on Seneca Falls automatic lathe.)

Frequently, such manual input provisions are adapted to a numerical tape control system to improve operational flexibility, as for on-off parts and short runs.

The various modes of operation that may be available may be illustrated with the 900 Series of numerical positioning control by Cutler-Hammer Inc., and with reference to its use on a large Wiedematic turret punch press (as built by Wiedemann Division, The Warner & Swasey Company):

1. *Automatic mode—the normal mode of operation for this system; the punched tape controls positioning and entire machine cycle.*
2. *Semi-automatic—with punched tape, but reading only one block at a time; cycles are initiated manually.*
3. *Dial input—the positioning and functional information as selected is manually dialed into the control system; no tape is required.*
4. *Manual mode—the machine is operated manually, using jog or pushbutton inching control.*

"MANUAL OPERATION" IN NC MANUFACTURING

The term "manual operation" when employed in connection with a numerically controlled machine in metalworking or related manufacturing, can have any one of several meanings. One is to indicate actual manual operation of the machine, as for instance, using a pushbutton inching or jog control. Neither tape nor dial numerical input is then employed. This type of operation is chiefly for setting up and checking purposes. Additional meanings of this elastic term are the use of dial numerical input, and the selection and use of a single block of information on the tape.

Conventional and Numerical Operation (as Alternatives)

In the application of general purpose machine tools, the main alternative choice to operation under numerical control is conventional or manual operation—the operator uses the power feeds and standard controls of the machine, but all functions are under his control—they are not "programmed," nor are they sequenced automatically.

The graph of Figure 13–7 compares production times of conventional press operations involving multiple tool setups, on notching presses and miscellaneous presses, with those of a tape controlled turret punch press, a Wiedematic A-30, as made by Wiedemann Division, The Warner & Swasey Company. The curves of the graph reflect savings of NC punch

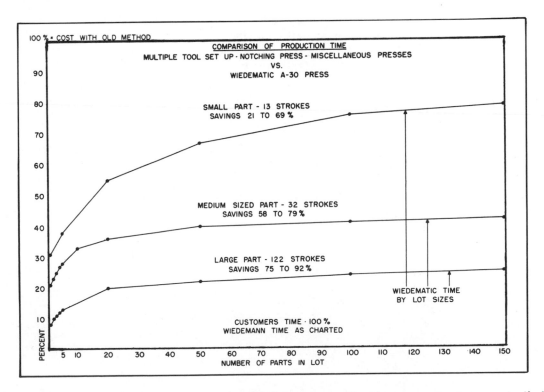

Figure 13–7. A comparison chart of production times—conventional presses vs. a tape controlled (Wiedematic) turret punch press. (Wiedemann Division, The Warner & Swasey Company.)

press operations. In each case, the area above the curve, to the top or 100 per cent line, represents the time saving under numerical control. The 100 percent figure (top left) represents the full cost under conventional methods; cost savings range from 60 per cent to 90 per cent, as shown. Press strokes range from 13 to 122 per part on these samples, as shown in the graph. Maximum lot size, as plotted, is 150 parts. Time savings range from 21 per cent to 92 per cent.

The machine involved in this comparison has a turret with 30 punches and dies (30 turret stations); it can carry out hole piercing at 200 strokes per min., and has a capacity of 30 tons. Positioning speed is up to 600 in. per min., and hole positioning accuracy is plus or minus 0.006 in.

Computer Operation of Machine Tools

Research and development work is in progress to adapt computers (such as general purpose types) directly to machine tool operation and to more manufacturing or industrial processes. Such work is being carried out both in the United States and in other countries. Computer operation of machines is closely associated with numerical control; continuous-path systems essentially use special-purpose computers as their central machine control units, sometimes referred to as directors. The machine control units of most other numerical control systems also employ some computer circuits.

Parts may be manufactured entirely with computer assistance, from and including the design stage to production by computer and tape control. Geometric descriptions in computer-routine language can take the place of drawings in design, followed by computer-oriented programming and production. Magnetic instead of punched tape may be favored. (Various regular continuous-path controls use magnetic tape in cartridge form; also, a system may have no internal interpolation, the detailed computing or interpolation for tool paths being made by computer at a central tape preparation service, which supplies a completed, magnetic control tape. Such a procedure is designed to reduce the capital cost of multi-axis continuous-path or contouring systems.)

CHAPTER FOURTEEN

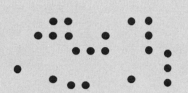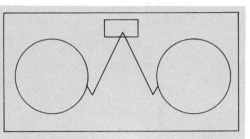

EFFECTS OF NUMERICAL CONTROL
AND NEW DEMANDS
ON A BUSINESS CAUSED
BY NUMERICAL CONTROL

THE INTRODUCTION OF NUMERICAL CONTROL ON AN INCREASING SCALE NATURALLY RAISES QUESTIONS SUCH AS THESE: WHAT WILL BE THE EFFECT ON MORALE IN YOUR PLANT IF YOU INTRODUCE EXTENSIVE NUMERICAL CONTROL INSTALLATIONS? WHAT WILL BE THE SOCIAL EFFECTS GENERALLY IF NUMERICAL CONTROL IS WIDELY USED THROUGHOUT INDUSTRY? TO WHAT EXTENT ARE OPERATORS, SKILLED AND OTHERWISE, REPLACED? AND WHAT ARE THE IMPLICATIONS IN CONNECTION WITH UNION CONTRACTS OR COLLECTIVE AGREEMENTS?

THE ANSWERS TO THESE QUESTIONS, ALTHOUGH THEY MAY NOT LOOM AS LARGE AS THE DIRECT ECONOMIC AND TECHNICAL ASPECTS OF AUTOMATION THROUGH NUMERICAL CONTROL, NEVERTHELESS REQUIRE A GOOD DEAL OF CONSIDERATION.

STILL OTHER QUESTIONS THAT MUST BE CON-

179

sidered are the important effects of numerical control on quality, and new demands that are placed on a business when numerical control is introduced.

Effects of Numerical Control on Plant Morale

WORK FORCE REDUCTIONS AND TRANSFERS

In any consideration of automation, as it affects the size of a plant's work force or shop staff, the question of layoffs comes to mind. And if automation does not result in layoffs, then readjustments or transfers within the plant will most certainly have to be considered.

The introduction of numerical control, in the manner that the concept is currently applied, has an overall effect which can be said to be intermediate between that resulting from necessary modernization of plant equipment and plant facilities on the one hand, and the introduction of automation of a fairly high degree on the other.

The effect on the size of the plant force cannot be compared with that when a high-production transfer line, for example, is being installed. Numerical control is basically automation for short and medium runs, except where machining centers with automatic tool changers and NC transfer lines are installed for medium to higher volume production. Then the overall effect is similar to that of instituting automation of a higher degree. The latter also holds true if a new plant is to be established—or new production lines set up—to use the "total" approach to numerical control, and where in addition, computers could take over many of the planning and programming functions.

OPERATOR REQUIREMENTS

The introduction of numerical control in a plant need not always mean that fewer machine operators are required, unless a very extensive changeover or plan of the previously mentioned type is involved. It has been found that, because numerically controlled machines are usually run for several shifts a day, additional operators, as obtained from replaced machines, may be required.

Also, there is the fact that the majority of numerical control installations do not dispense with the operator, but rather, that they increase productiviy. However, depending on the mode of operation employed, an operator may or may not be able to tend several machines instead of one. In the average plant, even this need not mean layoffs of shop staff—unless a considerable number of conventional machines are replaced—although it may require transfers to other machines or even to other departments within the plant or company.

The practice of having one operator looking after more than one machine is nothing new in itself, as it has been used with automatic screw machines and other automatics for many years. It is only when sudden changes are made through the installation of new equipment, especially in the case of numerical control or equipment of automatic or semi-automatic type, that shop-force requirements are affected. A collective agreement with a plant's union, concerning the operation of more than one machine by one operator for example, may then be affected at the same time.

Although one NC machine tool usually replaces several conventional machines, the number of operators required may remain almost the same as before, in individual cases, because the new machine is preferably operated on a multi-shift basis. Also, common practice is still to assign an operator to each NC machine. However, with fuller adoption of numerical control, an overall reduction in the required labor force must be foreseen.

IMPORTANCE OF ADVANCE PLANNING FOR STAFF CHANGES

If reductions in the plant force are foreseen, or numerous transfers within a plant must be undertaken, then preparations should be made well in advance. Invariably, they should include consultation with the employees who are affected, or with the union representing them. If layoffs are inevitable, then advance consultation will ease the problem for all concerned.

The problems of displacement of employees due to automation are of necessity receiving increasing attention in numerous industries that are affected by technological changes. If automation clauses providing for bonus settlements or payments as compensation for job loss are already included in a collective agreement, then part of the problem at least has been solved in advance. However, the advance consultation is still of considerable importance.

TRANSFERS WITHIN A PLANT

Instead of layoffs, however, transfers may be the solution in many cases. A reclassification of the jobs may have to be undertaken, and inter-departmental transfers made. Usually, this ties in with an analysis of the shop force as presently constituted, or at least of the operators who will be affected by transfers. This brings up the matter of retraining, which will be treated in later paragraphs.

If no reductions or transfers are necessary, then profit sharing agreements and incentive plans may still be affected, and may need re-evaluation or redefinition. Also, specific clauses of any collective agreement may be brought into play, or a raise in wages may be requested or be indicated in any case, when an operator is assigned to a more productive machine, even if it is in the same job category.

The advance planning and consultation, in the case of projected staff reductions or large-scale transfers, may advisedly be undertaken in collaboration with the interested government bodies, such as agencies of the United States Department of Labor. This can result in suitable placements in other plants or industries with the least inconvenience to all.

CONTRACT REQUIREMENTS

If a collective agreement or contract between a plant and its employees, or its affected employees, does not include any clauses providing for settlement or terms in the case of displacement due to automation or technological change, it is to the best interests of both management and employees to consider their inclusion in future contracts. This step can prevent much misunderstanding between management and a union, or between management and individual employees. At the same time, any such provisions, whether through a union or simply by management agreement, will do a great deal to increase and maintain morale throughout a plant.

Contract negotiations between labor and management in many industries in recent years have stressed automation provisions; agreements have included retirement provisions or settlements in the case of introduced automation and resultant possible layoffs, with the inclusion of additional safeguards from the standpoint of the employee.

More recently, and with increasing frequency, the contract terms sought by trade unions have included the guaranteed annual wage, more liberal pension provisions, and an increasing array of fringe benefits. Management cannot ignore such trends, and their due consideration should be undertaken, whether plant modernization, large scale installation of numerical control, or the introduction of other automation is being planned. Advance provisions will help prevent possible misunderstandings later, but at the same time, the anticipation of such contract demands cannot help but cause management to turn more and more toward more productive or more automated methods of manufacturing.

EMPLOYEE RELATIONS

Whether numerical control is a factor or not, it is a truism that the maintenance of contract terms during the life of an agreement, or rather their observance, should be sought by both sides.

Prompt settling of routine grievances, before they become big issues, is advisable under all circumstances. This can also prevent the occurrence of cases where the dismissal or correction of a plant employee can spark a plant shutdown, if the bargaining union thinks there has been a violation of its collective agreement.

Whenever union contracts are involved, it is of course always advisable to have frequent consultations between management and the union *before* negotiations take place at the bargaining table, in order to maintain good employee relations. Such a policy has proved its effectiveness.

Advance planning and all-around consideration of the above factors can do much to maintain good industrial relations and improve morale, when automation in any form is introduced, or important changes are made.

RETRAINING AND IN-PLANT TRANSFERS

Advance planning for the retraining of operators who may be displaced by the introduction of numerical control, for transfer to other departments within a plant, or to other machines or occupations in the same department, is just as important as advance planning to cope with possible layoffs. This planning for retraining should preferably be carried out as well in consultation and cooperation with an involved union. It will help to assure active cooperation in, and the success of, such a retraining program.

Retraining in this connection does not refer to the training of numerical control staff *per se*—that of programmers, or part programmers, operators of NC machines, and others— but to training in new skills to fit the displaced operators or employees into other jobs within the company. Valuable employees may be retained, and the retraining problems may often be much less involved than anticipated.

Analysis of Jobs and Skills—By carrying out an initial analysis of the job requirements or skills for various operators and occupations within a department, as well as within the entire plant—or at least in connection with operators who may have to be transferred to other departments—a retraining program can be simplified and started properly at the same time.

It will often come as a surprise to discover various talents or skills that plant employees possess, but which they are not required for use in the operation of their particular machine or in the execution of their current duties. An assessment of their potential is therefore as important as the job analysis and retraining are. For example, as fewer toolmakers are required with numerical control operation, some of them can advantageously be trained as programmers. Also, skilled operators with a fair background in mathematics may be suitable for training as inspectors, as another example.

Plant-Wide Job Analysis and Transfers—In other cases of retraining, it may be necessary to shift employees or transfer them to a different plant department entirely. The plant-wide job analysis helps particularly at this point. If none has been undertaken recently, it may be surprising to note just how many different job categories and qualifications may be involved.

In addition to the production force, which includes various basic categories such as setup men and operators with varying degrees of specialization, and machinists and other workers with all-around skills, there are other employees, in the plant maintenance staff, for example. These may have skills ranging all the way from those of the machinists and production workers, when machinery repairs are involved or servicing is required, to others concerned with the upkeep of buildings and of various other utilities serving a plant.

The introduction of numerical control or automated equipment demands that more stress be placed on areas such as process planning (which, however, is usually not a shop function) and servicing and planned maintenance of machines. Ordinarily, a large increase in the employment of maintenance personnel need not be projected. If a great amount of maintenance were necessary to keep NC machines going, they simply would not be installed.

More stress must also be placed on work involving electric and electronic circuits, hydraulics and pneumatics, in maintenance. Further general attention areas are in inspection —due to increased output, in incoming materials control, and other plant activity.

Further, there are the materials handling, assembly, and other workers and their skills classification to be considered.

All this affects the job analyses and the retraining policies adopted.

Developing Retraining Policies—Should this retraining be undertaken within the plant or elsewhere, or should it be some type of a divided effort between the plant and for instance, technical schools or vocational institutions? Because retraining may also involve upgrading in basic education as required for the new job, this part can best be done in classrooms, through proper arrangements.

The full services of the United States Department of Labor should be enrolled, or the Department's cooperation sought, in planning retraining programs, and the full cooperation of the employees enlisted.

The industry-wide or group approaches should also be studied, and this is another case where the applicable manufacturers' association can provide guidance and assistance. Government incentive programs and financial assistance may also be available, and these should be investigated.

Training and retraining programs with government assistance have been of prime importance, both in adapting the labor forces to changes in technological requirements, and in upgrading and training to improve employment opportunities generally. Numerous figures have been widely quoted on the number of workers displaced and replaced by automation annually, and they need not be repeated here.

Involvement in Problems of Automation—Automation *per se* is replacing workers each year in various industries, and although new avenues are being opened up through this automation, every manufacturer or employer, singly or in groups, is involved in this problem, whether he likes it or not.

It is unlikely that the smaller plants, installing numerically controlled machines with a degree of semi-automation only and on a relatively small scale, will feel great impact on manpower through the introduction of numerical control, but they too will have to do more planning on the social effects of automation.

POSITIVE FACTORS ENHANCING MORALE

The status of plant morale in relation to the introduction of numerical control, as applied to metalworking manufacturing plants, would appear to be a satisfactory one.

Shop morale in most plants with numerical control currently cannot be said to be suffering due to the introduction of this manufacturing concept. An upgrading of procedures usually required for NC operation brings challenges with it, which are met and which contribute to a sense of achievement. The psychological effect upon an operator, in relinquishing some of his duties over control of a machine, are generally balanced or overcome by positive factors. The operator may achieve a technician or setup man status, or the equivalent, which means a promotion for him. There is also the pride and prestige associated with a new process.

The NC operator can devote time to more important matters than engaging and disengaging feeds, changing speeds, and generally swinging machine levers around; he is more productively occupied when these functions are taken over by numerical control, and this in itself must result in the raising of morale and improvement in operator performance as such.

In conclusion, as to plant morale and the social effects of automation generally, it goes without saying that industry as a whole will be expected to assume a greater responsibility in the future to prepare and place plant workers who are displaced or forced out of an industry. Failure to do this could result in increased government intervention in the whole field of automation and labor or industrial relations problems.

Effects of Numerical Control on Quality

Uniformity of the finished product is an outstanding effect on quality when numerical control is introduced. Quality is more uniform from one part to the next because all of the parts are machined from the same tape, under predetermined conditions. This applies whether the control system used is basically of point-to-point type or the continuous-path kind.

Numerically controlled machines must be inherently more accurate than conventionally controlled ones, and this also applies to retrofitted machines. This in itself contributes to better quality of the product and greater uniformity.

Since production practices must also be geared to high efficiency, using the latest available tools and methods to insure economy as well as quality of production—in order to utilize the numerical control concept to best advantage—this is an additional inherent advantage that contributes to overall quality. This factor, as well as additional points, have been treated in previous chapters, and this section reviews some of them, with the inclusion of further points.

Both setup and operation are more reliable under tape controlled machining, and both have their beneficial effects on the uniformity of the part or product.

The improved uniformity applies to: basic dimensional accuracy (as to diameters, lengths, and angles—for example, in turning, boring and milling operations); in dimensional accuracy as it applies to the relationships between various dimensions (for example, hole spacing in drilling and boring); improved uniformity of contours where these are involved; the general geometry of a part; and then the surface finish, where machining operations are involved.

EXTRA QUALITY FROM POINT-TO-POINT OPERATIONS

In point-to-point or positioning operations, hole locations can be repeated time after time, frequently with greater accuracy than with the usual type of drilling jigs, or boring jigs, when the latter are employed. Drills, for example, are not restrained by drill jig bushings; therefore, there is less wear on the drills, and likewise, because chip elimination is less of a problem when no jigs need to be used, it increases the life of the cutting edges, and produces more uniform holes.

Due to the absence of a jig in a drilling operation, the coolant or cutting lubricant can be directed more readily to the exact cutting point, where it counts most. This applies likewise to tapping and other hole operations.

EXTRA QUALITY FROM CONTINUOUS-PATH OPERATION

In continuous-path operations or contouring, as in turning and milling operations, when compared with tracing, uniformity in general may be improved because the accuracy of the contour does not depend on the accuracy and setup of the tracing template or master. Similar results are obtained when step shafts, for example, are machined. Moreover, with numerical control also, all machine functions can be executed under predetermined conditions.

The results are more pronounced when complex contours are involved, as explained earlier in the comparisons between tracer control and numerical control. Complex jobs can be accurately programmed—mathematical definition of part geometry frequently taking the place of making the more difficult types of masters for tracer control. Tracing or copying will likely continue to play an important role, however, in applications where investment in continuous-path numerical control may not be justified.

DIMENSIONAL QUALITY AND OPERATOR RESPONSIBILITY

In most numerically controlled operations, especially in contour machining, the operating sequence or program is carried out as placed on the tape, and the part is run off under controlled conditions—the operator is prevented from making changes that basically affect the operation as programmed, or is not required to do so.

There are exceptions however, where the intervention of a skilled operator is required, depending also on the degree of automatic control that is being employed. "Manual" operation has already been explained, and the optional provision of manual override in a system makes it possible for the operator to compensate for tool wear or other machining factors.

In the operation of a larger vertical turret lathe, for example, it may be necessary to program additional stops on the tape at various points of a complete machining cycle, to permit the operator to make compensation for tool deflection, tool wear, or any misalignment. When such adjustments have been determined in a trial run, however, they may be programmed on tape for machining the entire lot with a minimum or absence of operator intervention. The research in and development of "adaptive controls" is intended to counter variations in cutting conditions that affect the dimensions and surface finish.

IMPROVED SURFACE FINISH

The contribution that numerical control makes to improved and more uniform surface finishes is an important effect that it has on quality. Surface finish is becoming increasingly more important, as more exacting work is demanded in the more specialized fields of manufacture. Also, greater uniformity in the finishes that are specified—the degrees of finish or "surface roughness"—has a marked bearing on the ease of assembly.

Surface finish as to roughness (irregularities), waviness, and flaws, can more readily be held within specified limits under numerical control. Surface finish can be more uniform due to the improved control over cutting conditions—cutting speeds, cutting feeds and others, which directly affect the life of the cutting edge and hence the results both as to surface finish and dimensional accuracy.

Selection of proper cutting speeds and feeds, and their maintenance, are important in controlling surface finish. Changes in cutting speeds—to keep peripheral speeds uniform when diameters vary, for example—can be programmed into the tape, to be made automatically. Although such possibilities also depend on the design and type of the machine itself, the newer machine tools designed particularly for use with numerical control are intended for full utilization of this control principle.

QUALITY CONTROL

Any quality control program should be easier to administer under numerically controlled manufacturing due to this greater obtained uniformity. With increasing competition, quality assumes greater importance both in the domestic and international markets, and numerical control can do much to improve and assure this quality.

Modern quality control must not be relaxed, however, under numerically controlled manufacturing. It can be expedited by numerically controlled inspection equipment, especially for first-off parts, and must generally use up-to-date inspection and quality control techniques.

EFFECT ON NEWER APPROACHES TO QUALITY AND RELIABILITY

The newer concepts of value engineering, reliability engineering, and value analysis, can be exploited more fully and applied more readily, in general, with numerically controlled production. Although these concepts—intended to provide greater reliability of a product and improved quality, while taking production economics into full account—are basically not new, they have been systematized to facilitate their application and provide more predictable results.

If a part or product is to be redesigned through value analysis, numerically controlled manufacturing in itself can be of considerable value here, as in the reliability and value engineering approaches.

New Demands on a Business Caused by Numerical Control

The demands that may be placed on a business after the introduction of numerical control—or before its introduction, as various preparations must be taken into account—have been evident in most of the previous chapters. The same applies largely to the precautionary measures the manufacturer may have to take. Some of the problems are discussed in this section, which will constitute a review of some of the previous points.

RESPONSIBILITY SHIFTED TO MANAGEMENT OR ADMINISTRATION

The main demand which is placed on a business by the introduction of numerical control is the shift of responsibility for the detailed planning of actual shop or manufacturing operations from the shop to the management or administration level. Once the decision to purchase and use numerically controlled equipment has been made, the management responsibility rests with the production engineering staff, which takes over many of the decisions normally made by the shop staff.

When instructions are programmed on tape, production or machine operations are not dependent on plant personnel, whether supervisory or of operating type. The operator cannot change the sequence of operations as he sees fit; the proper methods planning or production engineering at the outset is therefore of great importance.

All engineering and management departments or sections involved in any way with production must be prepared to accept more responsibility.

Under numerically controlled manufacturing, the role of management is enlarged and that of the plant floor is diminished, as far as determining production rates and operating conditions are concerned.

In order to insure profitable shop operations, when using the NC concept, it is not possible for a manufacturer or plant to use inferior or obsolescent equipment and then depend on the skill of individual operators, machinists, and setup men, to make up for the deficiency in the equipment.

The complete program may be placed on tape, but the machine itself must carry it out, with whatever additional assistance or supervision that have been assigned to the operator.

The competence and resources of management, including capital resources, therefore play a more important role, which is also true of automation generally.

Regular Reviews Essential—Once numerical control has been introduced and is functioning on whatever scale that has been adopted, it is also essential that management adopt a policy to review the progress of the project from time to time, to see that all the inherent advantages and characteristics that are provided by numerical tape control are put to work efficiently and exploited to maximum advantage. Otherwise, it may not be possible to realize the calculated or planned rate of return on the investment or to achieve the desired payback period.

INDUSTRIAL RELATIONS OF GREATER IMPORTANCE

As noted, whenever a greater degree of automation is introduced, planning must be directed to the possible displacement of workers, even if this may involve only transfers within the plant itself.

With the introduction into a plant of only a few general purpose NC machines, which are generally used with an operator, large staff reductions are ordinarily not involved. However, when a number of standard machines are replaced by a single numerically controlled machine, when an operator attends several tape controlled machines, or when NC production or machining centers are installed, various attendant labor problems have to be dealt with, as given earlier in this chapter.

Other Employment and Planning Factors—The introduction of numerical control can at times result in *increased* employment within the plant, rather than the reverse. To obtain maximum returns from the numerical control concept, NC machines should be operated on at least a two-shift basis, as a general rule; as pointed out, this normally means two operators.

Also, when one or more NC machining centers are installed, their greater output also requires a greater input of materials—these may take the form of castings, for example, which have to be rough machined on some dimensions or machined to provide locating surfaces, which may be done on other machine tools. Even when a machining or production center can carry out a large variety of operations, it may still be more economical to have some of them performed on other, less expensive machines, the machine-hour rates of which are not as high.

In the preceding respect, as in various others that deal with production engineering or process planning, numerically controlled manufacturing is no different from that of conventional manufacturing—good production planning practice is still required.

Use of numerical control may also generate new business which could not be obtained or undertaken before.

TRAINING AND RETRAINING

The entire question of training and retraining of staff consists of two main areas—the first, training of programmers and machine operators, and other affected shop and engineering personnel, which may also include upgrading in specific conventional areas, and the second, training or possibly retraining of plant personnel for other jobs within the plant.

Training of production engineering personnel, as noted, is usually not a great problem, as process planning, for example, still requires the same fundamental experience and knowledge, although it is even more important with numerical control, and the latter should be taken into consideration at every major step.

For shop personnel that may be entirely displaced in some cases, the required training for transfer to employment in some other industry becomes an inter-industry and government problem.

DEMANDS ON PRODUCT AND TOOL DESIGN

Basically, the flexibility afforded by numerical control—the simpler tooling that may be employed, the greater ease of machining from the solid, and similar factors—places less restrictions on product design than conventional manufacturing. However, in both cases, product design of course should always be attuned to economical manufacturing of the parts involved. To place special restrictions on design, however, in order to use numerical control efficiently, would be a detraction from it, rather than an advantage.

Changes are necessary in tool design and in the tool design department, because simple fixtures for the most part are used, and drilling jigs, for example, are practically eliminated.

Blueprints or part drawings should preferably be of numerical control type for reference use at the machines, to avoid unnecessary addition and checking to obtain absolute coordinate dimensions. Drawings should be standardized in this respect throughout a plant, wherever it is feasible to do so.

THE BENEFITS AND IMPORTANCE OF STANDARDIZATION

Standardizing tape formats, process or tooling sheets, program sheets, and tape punching or tape preparation equipment, is an important factor in successful numerically controlled manufacturing.

Universal fixtures, where applicable, are extremely helpful in positioning applications and can be adapted to various machines. In the selection of standard interchangeable tooling, good production or tool engineering practice is of even greater importance here than in conventional machine operation.

As for the tapes themselves, standard methods of tape identification, and methods of storing master and working tapes, should be evolved.

PROGRAMMING SERVICES

To what extent computer assisted routines can be economically applied and outside programming services used, including tape preparation, are subjects dealt with in Chapters 10, 11, and 12.

QUALITY CONTROL OVER INCOMING MATERIAL

To assist in achieving the increased uniformity of machined or manufactured parts of which numerical control is capable, incoming-materials control should be tightened up. The machinability of material should not vary beyond the preset limits from one batch to the next as delivered by the supplier. Uniform cutting conditions cannot be obtained when the physical properties that affect machining are not uniform in the materials that are fed to the machine. This holds true for all automatic and semi-automatic machining, where the operator cannot be relied upon to make frequent adjustments to compensate for tool wear or other cutting conditions.

Control should be tightened over all purchased materials: raw materials such as bar stock for machining, and plate or sheet for punch press or other press operations, etc.; stock in the form of forgings and castings; semi-finished or rough-machined components from subcontractors or suppliers; finished components or subassemblies from subcontractors (to provide the same ease of final assembly as that obtained from the parts produced under numerical control); also any tooling such as fixtures that may be ordered from the outside.

The incoming-materials control department should have full authority to reject shipments that are just on the borderline of acceptance, and the tool inspection department should have complete authority to reject any substandard tooling that may be delivered by a supplier.

The above also applies to intra-plant departments. If castings, for example, have non-uniform machinability, if the hardness varies beyond the tolerable limits, or hard spots are encountered, the entire shipment should be rejected, whether it is from the company's own foundry or from an outside one, and the trouble corrected on future deliveries. It is not economical to hold up a machining center, for example, where more than 30 tools may be idle, or where tools may have to be replaced due to one defective casting. Likewise, castings and forgings should not vary widely in critical dimensions, as this too affects the uniformity of machining and the results obtained. The same can be said of punch press operations, in connection with sheet and plate.

SUBSTITUTION OF MATERIALS

Where alternative materials, such as alternative steel grades, may be specified on a print or part drawing, it is extremely important that the mechanical and physical properties of the substituted material equal those of the original specifications. If one AISI or SAE steel specification, for instance, is replaced by others, the specifications of the new or substituted steels must fall within their respective official specifications, or as may have been determined before by the engineering department during the design of the part.

It goes without saying also that substitutions should not be made on the plant floor without the consent of the affected engineering department.

MAINTAINING HIGH INSPECTION STANDARDS

To accompany the higher uniformity and quality available from numerically controlled production, a high level of inspection standards should be maintained. Although it should be possible to reduce overall inspection costs, the necessary inspection services should not be allowed to drop in efficiency.

Proper inspection and quality control are as important with numerical as well as with conventional machining or manufacturing. Although the operational program is placed on tape, for the machine to carry out, the actual work is still performed by the cutting or other tools. These must still be kept sharp, properly set up and adjusted, and monitored during operation and/or replaced at definite intervals.

These remarks apply to both parts inspection as well as gage and tool inspection. For extremely accurate work, the operator may be supplied with special precision measuring equipment at the machine itself, a practice which is also applied in conventional manufacturing to components requiring this type of treatment.

PERIODIC MACHINE INSPECTION AND MAINTENANCE

The importance of organizing the maintenance function was already stressed. The frequency of inspection and servicing—as applied to mechanical, electrical and electronic, hydraulic and other members or elements—must be increased proportionately when machines are run in several shifts instead of only one.

Machines must generally be kept in better condition than with conventional production, as in all automatic or semi-automatic operation. Since the flexibility of numerical control permits scheduling of machine loads or production runs at shorter notice, it is particularly critical that the machines and their systems be kept in top condition at all times to avoid delays and interrupted schedules.

Keeping well organized records, and even checking the efficiency of the record keeping itself, are indispensable in the organization of a regular maintenance program. The record should in itself assist in determining the effectiveness of maintenance procedures, most of which should be of preventive nature.

Spare machine parts of critical nature, and lists of parts, as supplied by the manufacturer, should be kept on hand. Recommendations of machine tool and systems builders should be followed on specific points. For the systems themselves, spare plug-in modules or units should be kept on hand, and system testing equipment as supplied or recommended by manufacturers, obtained and freely used. Proper briefing and additional in-plant training of maintenance staff, in the various mechanical, electrical and electronic areas, as may be required, should be undertaken in advance, it can be emphasized again.

RE-EVALUATING PRODUCTION CONDITIONS AND TECHNIQUES

As another reminder, the adoption of numerical control should be accompanied or preceded by a re-evaluation of machining conditions, in the case of machine tools—cutting speeds, cutting feeds, tool selection, tool geometry, and the like—and similar re-evaluations should be carried out from time to time as a regular procedure after numerical control is installed.

The manufacturing techniques themselves should likewise be reviewed from time to time, to be kept competitive and up to date with latest practices.

NC REQUIRES PARALLEL MODERNIZATION

In addition to providing a new or different concept of manufacturing, numerical control is also modernization *per se*. It is a method and a policy for keeping up to date in products and services as well as in manufacturing technology.

For these reasons, it is also necessary to modernize or up-date all other services as well—production control, materials flow and control, inventory control, etc. It is not possible to join obsolescent methods to a new concept.

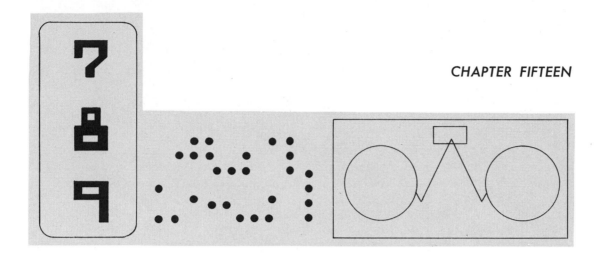

CHAPTER FIFTEEN

MAKING THE MOST OF NUMERICAL CONTROL FROM A PROFIT STANDPOINT

ONCE NUMERICAL CONTROL HAS BEEN ADOPTED IN A PLANT, WITH ONE OR ANY NUMBER OF INSTALLATIONS, IT IS UP TO MANAGEMENT TO MAKE THE MOST OF NUMERICAL CONTROL FROM A PROFIT STANDPOINT. FOLLOWING ARE SUGGESTIONS FOR UTILIZING THIS FORM OF AUTOMATION TO BEST ADVANTAGE IN THE VARIOUS OPERATIONAL AREAS.

1. Keeping Proper Cost Studies of All NC Production

SINCE NEW FACTORS ARE INTRODUCED IN USING THE NC MANUFACTURING CONCEPT, IT IS SPECIALLY IMPORTANT TO KEEP PROPER COST STUDIES OF ALL NC JOBS OR PRODUCTION RUNS. THESE WILL MAKE IT POSSIBLE TO IDENTIFY ANY FAULTS OR WEAKNESSES IN ANY PARTICULAR APPROACH AND WILL HELP GREATLY ON REPEAT JOBS and in rescheduling, as well as in estimating. Detailed records form a fund of experience which can be added to as time goes on. It is well to remember that estimating procedures will be somewhat different from those used when conventional manufacturing is employed, because inventories, tooling, and other factors, are viewed in a new light.

Careful cost studies promote continuous cost investigations and comparisons with conventional operation, which will also help to pinpoint or identify any areas where the advantages of numerical control are not fully utilized.

2. Adding Products and Markets

Because numerical control provides considerable flexibility in manufacturing and reduces the time required to launch a new product, it pays to look into the manufacture of specialty or custom products. As an additional outlet for capacity, it may be possible to produce these profitably in small or medium quantities. A shorter or transient market demand for any specialty items may be offset by the lower investment in NC tooling.

Adding subcontract jobs when the numerically controlled equipment is not operating at a near capacity may be possible, as the plant may be able to bid on numerous jobs that were beyond reach before. As a subcontractor, using numerically controlled production, it should be easier to channel parts directly into the production line of the client or of a prime contractor, and to do this much more readily than with conventional production facilities; in any case, it should allow the customer to save on inventory costs.

Prototype work, and special toolmaking orders, can frequently provide additional volume, or offer a field for specialization, especially to the smaller plant or job shop having numerical control.

Although the greatly shortened lead time is often a particularly important factor in bidding successfully for custom business, it should not be taken for granted that the mere mention of numerical control by itself will obtain the contracts—it is still necessary to point out and prove all the advantages offered.

DIVERSIFICATION

A policy of diversification can be assisted considerably with NC manufacturing. The new products or services—and the reference here is not to specialty items in particular—need not serve the same industries or customers as before. Entirely new products, although geared to the available production equipment and plant facilities, should be based on special management abilities, capital resources, and management potential. Diversification need not necessarily proceed in obvious directions in which competitors may be starting as well; this is a common occurrence and may defeat the purpose.

Necessity to diversify may be closely linked with product obsolescence—and numerical control can play an important part in reacting to this problem.

OFFERING SPECIALIZED TECHNIQUES

In offering NC production services, emphasis should be placed on specialized capabilities of NC systems which may meet a customer's urgent requirements. For example, mirror images—producing right and left hand parts of the same design—an economical procedure under numerical control, also enlargement and reduction in the size of a required part, may fit such special requirements.

The economics of numerical control, when applied to any of the preceding additional revenue areas, including specialty products manufacturing, subcontracting, diversification of products or services, or in offering specialized techniques, are available to small or large plant alike, as numerically controlled manufacturing need not depend on high volume to make it profitable.

3. Using Services of Machine or System Makers

It is advisable to utilize to the fullest extent the technical and consulting services offered by the machine tool builders and makers of other NC equipment, and by system manufacturers. This should start with the advance training for programmers and NC machine operators, machinists or technicians, and others, as emphasized before, including training for maintenance and all other affected activities.

This consultation, which begins with the projected investment in NC equipment, should not end with its installation. Both the machine builder and the system manufacturer—if they are not one and the same—can advise on problems which have been solved for or with the help of their other clients, and it is to the best interests of these suppliers as well to see that every plant becomes and remains a satisfied client.

4. Custom Computer Programming Services

For intricate contours, or if there is a great deal of production in which computer programming would be helpful, or if considerable variety of work is involved, then outside computer programming services, including tape preparation, should be investigated. This does not call for additional capital investment; on the other hand, investment in a suitable computer, or its rental, may be justified, especially when a general purpose computer is involved and which would also be used for additional functions in the company's operations.

Conversely, a plant specializing in numerical control manufacturing may itself be in a position to undertake such work for smaller NC shops in the area.

Not limited to contour applications, computer routines are of special value also in positioning work where irregular hole patterns, with a great many holes in a small area, are involved, and when programmers are overloaded with lengthy programs.

5. Keeping Abreast of Improved Engineering Materials

New and improved materials such as new alloy steel specifications are being continually developed and introduced on a commercial basis. Keeping product designs up to date and economical with reference to the most suitable and economical engineering materials, is perhaps more important with numerical control because of the higher payback rate required on the equipment.

If stainless steels, for instance, are being used extensively, it pays to investigate the latest "free-machining" or easier machining stainless steel grades or types.

Keeping up to date with the greater variety of engineering or machinery steels, and the types with somewhat leaner alloy contents, which have been introduced to supplant others where they are applicable, is advisable. On the other end of the scale, steels with extremely high tensile strengths have been developed and should be kept in mind as well.

Continual contact with developments in both ferrous and nonferrous metals should be maintained, including the field of light metals—aluminum and magnesium alloys. Plastics and other synthetics should be considered, where they may fit in properly, keeping in mind that these materials appear to be misapplied more frequently than any other types.

A periodic review of all areas of free machining or free working steels, where they can be applied suitably to cut down metal cutting and metal forming costs, can pay dividends. Also, it pays to watch developments in the less commonly used materials, but which are finding increasing applications as engineering materials in manufacturing—titanium and its alloys, tungsten, beryllium, molybdenum, and others.

In addition, the use of *standard* preformed shapes—for example, in the line of castings, forgings, and extrusions—going beyond those which are cast or formed specifically for a particular product or part, can effect notable economies in specific cases.

6. Keeping Abreast of Cutting Tool Materials, Production Techniques

Evaluating *all* cutting tool materials for cutting or forming of metals and other materials, including newer ones, for every major NC operation, is good policy. These tool materials include the improved or "super" high speed steels, "super" carbides, ceramics or cemented oxides, and cast alloy cutting tool materials, as well as diamonds (the latter usually for high speed finish turning operations on abrasive materials or for extremely fine finishes and particularly accurate sizing), and other cutting materials or grades under development.

For example, although a plant may not wish to consider ceramics as cutting tools for general machining, where the super carbides may be superior, depending on the application, ceramics have their place in high speed finishing and semifinishing operations. Their use may mean that spindle speeds need not be changed for a particular component, in a production cycle requiring numerous operations.

Consulting cutting tool manufacturers for the latest recommendations on grades, cutting speeds and feeds, depths of cut, cutting fluids, and other operating conditions, can result in substantial savings. The same applies to forming tool steels, or tool and die steels, and other materials used for forming tools, especially in view of the many improved types and grades that are being made available.

Additional and continued attention can profitably be paid to developments in indexable, throw-away type inserts for production runs in turning, boring, milling and related operations. Their use has the effect of preset tooling, so important in NC machining, especially with single-point tools. As with inserts in general practice, costs saved in the sharpening or regrinding that is eliminated with the inserts, also the savings in setup times, must be balanced against the number of cuts or parts obtained per cutting edge. At the same time, the comparisons with costs of conventional tool bits must be made.

Continued developments and improvements in inserts, available both in carbides and cemented oxides, have produced such results as the carbide insert design of Figure 15–1, where a micrometer and pencil provide size comparison. The molded-in grooves just back of the cutting edges eliminate separate chip breakers, in these inserts by Carmet Company, Allegheny Ludlum Steel Corp.

EVALUATING NEW TOOL DESIGNS

Investigating and evaluating the latest cutting and forming tool designs and tool holding methods, with a view to their adoption, is of increased importance with numerical control.

Figure 15–1. A development in indexable carbide inserts. Molded grooves at cutting edges eliminate chip breakers. (Carmet Co., Allegheny Ludlum Steel Corp.)

For any production run, greater attention should also be paid to the scheduling of regular cutting tool changes, to keep downtime to a minimum, instead of waiting for tools to become dull. Preset cutting tools to save time in setup and tool changing, should be favored, and are essential in a majority of cases, to cut downtime when making setups.

PRODUCTION OR PROCESS TECHNIQUES

It is well to keep in mind also that some of the more recent manufacturing methods or processes, and further advances in such methods as electrical discharge machining, plasma-arc cutting, electron beam welding, and others, including some specialized and advanced metal forming operations, may be accompanied by additional numerical control applications.

7. Exploiting the Simpler NC Tooling; Using Power Chucking Methods

The simpler fixturing or holding that is possible with operations on NC machine tools should be used to the fullest extent. The use of subplates or grid plates, and special or auxiliary work tables, to facilitate clamping and locating of workpieces on machine tables,

195

saves considerable setup time as well as sparing the surface of the table proper. Simple clamping devices such as toggle clamps frequently suffice for flat pieces, which, in addition, can often be stacked for drilling.

Universal work-holding tooling has been developed, such as universal tables with quick acting clamps, various simple locating devices or stops, and the necessary brackets, which in total will accommodate a wide variety of drilling, boring, tapping, milling, counterboring, reaming and related operations on general purpose NC drilling-milling machines and other types.

However, if parts require more elaborate fixtures, either to facilitate secure holding or initial locating on the machine table, then these special fixtures should be properly designed and built, to eliminate unnecessary downtime in setting up, and to permit proper machining. Attempts to save money with inadequate fixtures in such cases have the opposite effect.

For the larger machining centers, pallets for fast work loading and continuous machining, precision rotary indexing tables for horizontal machines and indexing trunnions for vertical machines (to permit operations on a number of work faces or sides in one setting), also additional work holding accessories or tooling, developed for these machines, should be utilized to maximum advantage.

The use of quick-change tool holders, wherever it speeds up operations, as well as the use of tool presetting facilities, are likewise specially important.

POWER CHUCKING AND POWER CLAMPING

Applying power operated chucking and work-holding devices whenever possible and practicable, ranging from fast acting air operated devices on drilling machines to heavy duty power operated chucks on the larger turret lathes and other machine tools, is indispensable in many NC operations.

Using power chucking on as many lathe operations as possible permits operators, being relieved of manual chucking, to turn out more and better work. Additionally, if a semi-automatic or automatic cycle is used, application of a power chuck or power work-holding device is frequently a critical, cost-cutting factor, and may be indispensable.

8. Regular Productivity Reviews

Keeping all machines in a plant under continuous review to detect possible obsolescence and to assure the planned-for productivity, is an important precaution. This applies to conventional as well as numerically controlled machines, although the latter, because of their greater flexibility, have the edge over conventional machines with regard to obsolescence. The MAPI urgency rating can be of considerable assistance in this regard (see Chapter 9).

The continuous review of productivity should also be maintained to assure that the higher returns generally necessary from an investment in numerically controlled equipment are being realized. Such reviews will also reveal if any of the features of numerical control equipment are not being used to full advantage.

9. Watching New Developments

Keeping all communications open to continue being in touch with new developments in applications of numerical control, improved programming methods, system features that may be added or changed, and complementary or alternative controls that may be put to work alongside numerical controls, according to the most suitable application of each, should be an essential part of company policy. Production, inspection, assembly, and any other areas of manufacturing, should be considered in this regard.

10. Research, and Building a Technological-Change Fund

Research in manufacturing techniques and products—also fundamental research where it can be done—is of increasing importance in competitive manufacturing. Making continuing research into numerical control and its applications a special project, where possible, is an advisable course for the user. Although numerical control may become known under a different name in the future, and proceed in additional and different directions under the spur of research and development work, this continued advance is bound to exploit the aspects of the basic numerical control concept.

It is well, for the manufacturer, to keep in mind the advisability of building up a research and technological-change fund, to assist his entire organization to adapt to the demands of the rapidly changing technological world.

The working of metals and other materials, as well as their production, and manufacturing operations or processing in other areas of industry, are becoming increasingly dependent on automation, and of the type that numerical control has to offer.

INDEX